CHEM 1112

Texas Southmost College

CENGAGE
Learning™

Australia • Brazil • Japan • Korea • Mexico • Singapore • Spain • United Kingdom • United States

CENGAGE
Learning™

CHEM 1112

Executive Editor:
Michael Stranz

Managing Lab Editor:
Jeff Nunn

Custom Lab Editors:
Cooper Gouge, John Horvath

Custom Production Editor:
Jennifer Flinchpaugh

Project Coordinators:
Lisa Donahue. Peg Hagar

Senior Pre-Press Specialist:
Riley Gibb

Production Supervisor-Labs:
Melanie Evans

Rights and Permissions Specialist:
Kalina Ingham Hintz

Senior Marketing Coordinator:
Sara Mercurio

For product information and technology assistance, contact us at
Cengage Learning Customer & Sales Support, 1-800-354-9706

For permission to use material from this text or product,
submit all requests online at **cengage.com/permissions**
Further permissions questions can be emailed to
permissionrequest@cengage.com

ISBN-13: 978-0-534-47529-1

ISBN-10: 0-534-47529-9

Cengage Learning
5191 Natorp Blvd.
Mason, OH 45040
USA

Cengage Learning is a leading provider of customized learning solutions with office locations around the globe, including Singapore, the United Kingdom, Australia, Mexico, Brazil, and Japan. Locate your local office at:
international.cengage.com/region

Cengage Learning products are represented in Canada by Nelson Education, Ltd.

Visit Signature Labs online at **signaturelabs.com**

Visit our corporate website at **cengage.com**

Printed in the United States of America

Acknowledgements

The content of this text has been adapted from the following product(s):

ANAL0366: The Chemistry and Qualitative Analysis of Cations: Groups III and IV
ISBN-10: (0-87540-366-2)
ISBN-13: (978-0-87540-366-3)

KINE0505: Studying the Rate of the Reaction of Potassium Permanganate and Oxalic Acid
ISBN-10: (0-87540-505-3)
ISBN-13: (978-0-87540-505-6)

EQUL0494: Monitoring Acid–Base Titrations with a pH Meter
ISBN-10: (0-87540-494-4)
ISBN-13: (978-0-87540-494-3)

ANAL0365: The Chemistry and Qualitative Analysis of Cations: Group II
ISBN-10: (0-87540-365-4)
ISBN-13: (978-0-87540-365-6)

EQUL0392: Introducing Equilibrium
ISBN-10: (0-87540-392-1)
ISBN-13: (978-0-87540-392-2)

ANAL0364: The Chemistry and Qualitative Analysis of Cations: Group Separations and Separations of Group I Cations
ISBN-10: (0-87540-364-6)
ISBN-13: (978-0-87540-364-9)

TECH0363: Laboratory Techniques: Qualitative Inorganic Analysis Techniques
ISBN-10: (0-87540-363-8)
ISBN-13: (978-0-87540-363-2)

TECH0488: Making and Using Visible Absorption Measurements
ISBN-10: (0-87540-488-X)
ISBN-13: (978-0-87540-488-2)

ELEC0450: Studying Electrochemical Half-Cells and Half-Reactions
ISBN-10: (0-87540-450-2)
ISBN-13: (978-0-87540-450-9)

ANAL0367: The Chemistry and Qualitative Analysis of Anions
ISBN-10: (0-87540-367-0)
ISBN-13: (978-0-87540-367-0)

Table Of Contents

The Chemistry and Qualitative Analysis of Cations: Group Separations and Separation of Group I Cations

Prepared by James G. Boyles, Bates College, and
Judith C. Foster and David S. Page, Bowdoin College

PURPOSE OF THE EXPERIMENT

Develop the chemistry of cation Groups I, II, and III. Demonstrate the separation of Groups I, II, and III, using Ag^+, Cu^{2+}, and Fe^{3+} ions. Establish a procedure for qualitatively verifying the presence of Ag^+, Hg_2^{2+}, and Pb^{2+} ions in an unknown solution.

BACKGROUND INFORMATION

A selected group of chemically important and commonly encountered cations appears in Table 1 on the next page. Although the chemistry of all 12 of these cations is discussed here, the laboratory portion of this experiment only involves five of these cations: Ag^+, Hg_2^{2+}, Pb^{2+}, Cu^{2+}, and Fe^{3+} ions. The unique chemical properties of each cation makes it possible to separate and verify its presence, even in complex mixtures.

One of the simplest but most successful ways to separate one metal cation from another in a mixture is **selective precipitation**. Thus, one or more cations in solution can be precipitated from other cations in the same solution by the addition of various reagents followed by relatively simple manipulations.

When this approach is adopted, two questions immediately arise. Which one of several possible reagents is best? How much of this reagent should be used? The answer to the first question requires a knowledge of the relative solubilities, hence, the solubility product constants (K_{sp}), of potential precipitated compounds. The answer to the second question depends on the extent to which the separation must be quantitative. However, even if only a qualitative separation is desired, as in this

Table 1 *Nomenclature and formulas of 12 important cations*

cation	common name	formula
barium		Ba^{2+}
bismuth(III)		Bi^{3+}
calcium		Ca^{2+}
cadmium(II)		Cd^{2+}
chromium(III)	chromic	Cr^{3+}
copper(II)	cupric	Cu^{2+}
iron(III)	ferric	Fe^{3+}
lead(II)	plumbous	Pb^{2+}
mercury(I)	mercurous	Hg_2^{2+}
nickel(II)	nickelous	Ni^{2+}
silver(I)		Ag^+
tin(IV)	stannic	Sn^{4+}

experiment, a calculation is required involving solubility product constants and concentrations of various species in solution.

Before carrying out this experiment, we must first find answers to these two questions. Then, we must design a set of procedures and manipulations that will allow the application of this knowledge in the laboratory.

The cations listed in Table 1 are commonly divided into four groups on the basis of their chemical behavior to the chloride ion (Cl^-) and the sulfide ion (S^{2-}). First we will discuss the separation of Group I, II, III, and IV cations as groups of cations. Then, we will consider the separation of individual Group I cations.

I. Separating Group I Cations from Group II, III, and IV Cations

Of the several anions that could be added as precipitating reagents, only two, Cl^- and S^{2-}, will be considered initially. **Chloride ion** is the anion of the strong acid hydrochloric acid (HCl). It is therefore a weak Brønsted base and undergoes negligible hydrolysis in aqueous solution. The only equilibria that need to be considered, then, are solubility equilibria of the type

$$Ag^+(aq) + Cl^-(aq) \rightleftharpoons AgCl(s, \text{ white}) \qquad \text{(Eq. 1)}$$

and, under appropriate conditions, complex ion equilibria of the type

$$Ag^+(aq) + 2\ Cl^-(aq) \rightleftharpoons [AgCl_2]^-(aq) \qquad \text{(Eq. 2)}$$

Sulfide ion is the anion of the weak acid HS^-. It is a strong Brønsted base and undergoes extensive hydrolysis in aqueous solution, as shown in Equation 3.

$$S^{2-}(aq) + HOH(l) \rightleftharpoons HS^-(aq) + OH^-(aq) \qquad \text{(Eq. 3)}$$

In discussing the more complicated sulfide acid–base equilibria, it is helpful to consider first the source of S^{2-} ion and then how the various equilibria involved can be manipulated to obtain the desired S^{2-} ion concentration.

When thioacetamide (CH_3CSNH_2) is dissolved in water, the following equilibrium is established:

$$CH_3\text{-}\overset{\overset{\displaystyle S}{\|}}{C}\text{-}NH_2(aq) + 2\,HOH(l) \rightleftharpoons$$

$$CH_3\text{-}\overset{\overset{\displaystyle O}{\|}}{C}\text{-}O^-(aq) + NH_4^+(aq) + H_2S(g) \qquad \text{(Eq. 4)}$$

The forward reaction in this equilibrium is endothermic. The application of heat causes the reaction to produce increased concentrations of products, in accordance with Le Châtelier's principle. A warm solution of thioacetamide serves as a convenient in situ source of hydrogen sulfide (H_2S). In aqueous solution, H_2S is involved in the following acid–base equilibria:

$$H_2S(aq) + H_2O(l) \rightleftharpoons H_3O^+(aq) + HS^-(aq) \qquad \text{(Eq. 5)}$$

$$K_{a_1} = \frac{[H_3O^+]\,[HS^-]}{[H_2S]} = 1.0 \times 10^{-7} \qquad \text{(Eq. 6)}$$

$$HS^-(aq) + H_2O(l) \rightleftharpoons H_3O^+(aq) + S^{2-}(aq) \qquad \text{(Eq. 7)}$$

$$K_{a_2} = \frac{[H_3O^+]\,[S^{2-}]}{[HS^-]} = 1.3 \times 10^{-13} \qquad \text{(Eq. 8)}$$

Application of Le Châtelier's principle allows us to predict that an increase in the hydronium ion (H_3O^+) concentration in a solution containing H_2S will result in a decrease in the S^{2-} ion concentration, while a decrease in the H_3O^+ ion concentration will result in an increase in the S^{2-} ion equilibrium concentration. Thus, the S^{2-} ion concentration in a solution saturated with H_2S can be controlled by adjusting the acidity of the solution. When Equation 5 and 7 are combined, the overall dissociation of H_2S may be described with a single chemical equation and a single equilibrium expression. Addition of Equation 5 and 7 gives

$$H_2S(aq) + 2\,H_2O(l) \rightleftharpoons 2\,H_3O^+(aq) + S^{2-}(aq) \qquad \text{(Eq. 9)}$$

and multiplication of the correponing equilibrium expressions gives

$$\left(\frac{[H_3O^+]\,[HS^-]}{[H_2S]} \right) \left(\frac{[H_3O^+]\,[S^{2-}]}{[HS^-]} \right) = \frac{[H_3O^+]^2\,[S^{2-}]}{[H_2S]} = K_{a_1}\,K_{a_2} = K_{H_2S} \qquad \text{(Eq. 10)}$$

In conventional notation schemes, the square brackets indicate concentration in moles per liter.

By using the equilibrium constants given above, we can obtain the overall equilibrium constant.

$$K_{H_2S} = K_{a_1} K_{a_2}$$
$$= (1.0 \times 10^{-7})(1.3 \times 10^{-13}) \qquad \text{(Eq. 11)}$$
$$= 1.3 \times 10^{-20}$$

The overall equilibrium expression in Equation 10 may be used to calculate the H_3O^+ or S^{2-} ion concentration in a solution saturated with H_2S when either concentration is known. Both H_3O^+ and S^{2-} ion concentrations cannot be solved for simultaneously by using this relation because there would be one equation and two unknowns. To illustrate the use of this equilibrium expression, we can determine the S^{2-} ion concentration in a solution that is 1.0×10^{-2} M in H_2S. By rearranging the overall equilibrium expression (Equation 10) as follows

$$[S^{2-}] = \frac{[H_2S](1.3 \times 10^{-20})}{[H_3O^+]^2} = \frac{1.3 \times 10^{-22}}{[H_3O^+]^2} \qquad \text{(Eq. 12)}$$

we can see that the equilibrium S^{2-} ion concentration is inversely proportional to the square of the H_3O^+ ion concentration. By controlling the H_3O^+ ion concentration, that is, by controlling the pH of the solution, we can control the S^{2-} ion concentration. This concentration, in turn, will determine which metal sulfide will precipitate from solution. Table 2 gives the S^{2-} ion concentration in equilibrium with 1.0×10^{-2}M H_2S at various H_3O^+ ion concentrations and pH values.

Now we will consider the problem of deciding which of these two reagents, Cl^- or S^{2-} ion, will more easily and efficiently effect a separation of the larger group of cations into smaller subgroups. Examination of the solubility product constants given in Table 3 is revealing. Of the 12 cations being considered, only three, Ag^+, Hg_2^{2+}, and Pb^{2+} ions, form reasonably insoluble chlorides. These cations are commonly referred to as Group I cations or **insoluble chlorides**.

Therefore, a procedure of separation becomes evident. Hydrochloric acid serves as an ideal source of Cl^- ion because H_3O^+ ion is not involved in any interfering equilibria with Ag^+ ion, Hg_2^{2+} ion, Pb^{2+} ion, or any of the other cations remaining in solution. First, we add HCl to a solution containing the 12 specified cations. Ag^+ ion, Hg_2^{2+} ion, and/or Pb^{2+} ion will precipitate as insoluble silver chloride (AgCl), mercury(I) chloride (Hg_2Cl_2, mercurous chloride), and/or lead(II) chloride ($PbCl_2$, plumbous chloride). The precipitate can be separated from the solution containing the other cations by filtration or centrifugation. The mixture of insoluble chlorides can then be further separated and individually identified.

Table 2 *Equilibrium concentrations of S^{2-}ion in 1.0×10^{-2}M H_2S solutions of various hydrogen ion concentrations*

solution	pH	S^{2-} ion concentration, mol L^{-1}
1.0×10^{-2}M H_2S	4.5	1.3×10^{-13}
1.0×10^{-2}M $H_2S + 1.0 \times 10^{-3}$ M H_3O^+	3	1.3×10^{-16}
1.0×10^{-2}M $H_2S + 1.0 \times 10^{-2}$M H_3O^+	2	1.3×10^{-18}
1.0×10^{-2}M $H_2S + 0.10$M H_3O^+	1	1.3×10^{-20}
1.0×10^{-2}M $H_2S + 1.0$M H_3O^+	0	1.3×10^{-22}

Table 3 *Solubility product constants at 25 °C*

ion	chloride	sulfide	minimum $[S^{2-}]$ needed to precipitate 0.1M cations
Ag^+	1.8×10^{-10}	6.8×10^{-50}	—
Hg_2^{2+}	1.3×10^{-18}	5.8×10^{-44}	—
Pb^{2+}	1.6×10^{-5}	8.4×10^{-28}	—
Cu^{2+}	$>10^{-1}$ (soluble)	8.7×10^{-36}	8.7×10^{-35}
Cd^{2+}	$>10^{-1}$ (soluble)	7.8×10^{-27}	7.8×10^{-26}
Bi^{3+}	$>10^{-1}$ (soluble)	6.8×10^{-97}	4.1×10^{-32}
Sn^{4+}	$>10^{-1}$ (soluble)	$SnS_2 = 1.0 \times 10^{-70}$	3.2×10^{-35}
Fe^{2+}	$>10^{-1}$ (soluble)	$FeS = 4.9 \times 10^{-18}$	4.9×10^{-17}
Fe^{3+}	$>10^{-1}$ (soluble)	$Fe_2S_3 = 1 \times 10^{-88*}$	$2.2 \times 10^{-29*}$
Ni^{2+}	$>10^{-1}$ (soluble)	1.8×10^{-21}	1.8×10^{-20}
Cr^{3+}	$>10^{-1}$ (soluble)	not stable in H_2O	—
Ba^{2+}	$>10^{-1}$ (soluble)	not stable in H_2O	—
Ca^{2+}	$>10^{-1}$ (soluble)	not stable in H_2O	—

* Fe_2S_3 in acid decomposes to FeS and S.

The cations remaining in the filtrate can be separated and individually identified.

Although these Group I chlorides are very insoluble, their solubilities vary quite a bit. If we add enough chloride to precipitate virtually all of the most soluble of the three chlorides, $PbCl_2$, then we may be assured the other two more insoluble Group I chlorides are even more completely precipitated.

How much Cl^- ion should be used for the precipitation? Consider the most soluble chloride of the three Group I cations, $PbCl_2$, as an example:

$$PbCl_2(s, \text{ white}) \rightleftharpoons Pb^{2+}(aq) + 2\,Cl^-(aq) \qquad \text{(Eq. 13)}$$

$$[Pb^{2+}]\,[Cl^-]^2 = K_{sp} = 1.6 \times 10^{-5} \qquad \text{(Eq. 14)}$$

The left side of Equation 14 is called the **ion product**, while the right side is the K_{sp}. In a given solution, precipitation will begin to occur only when the ion product exceeds the solubility product constant. If the object is to precipitate the Pb^{2+} ions, a high Cl^- ion concentration, according to Le Châtelier's principle, will force the reaction shown in Equation 13 to the left. Thus, the Pb^{2+} ion will be virtually completely precipitated.

Addition of Cl^- ion will have no noticeable effect until enough has been added. Because of the Pb^{2+} ion already present when enough Cl^- has been added, the ion product exceeds the solubility product and precipitation occurs. It is important to note that prior to the formation of solid precipitate, addition of Cl^- ion does not shift the equilibrium of Equation 13. Indeed, there can be no equilibrium situation unless some $PbCl_2(s)$ is present. After some solid $PbCl_2$ is present, further addition of Cl^- ion shifts the equilibrium to the left in what is known as the **common-ion effect**. This equilibrium shift reduces the solubility of $PbCl_2$ and the concentration of Pb^{2+} ion remaining in solution. If Pb^{2+} ion is initially present at a concentration of 0.10M, precipitation will occur when the Cl^- ion reaches a concentration such that the ion product of Pb^{2+} ion and Cl^- ion just exceeds the solubility product constant 1.6×10^{-5}. This precipitation occurs when

$$[Cl^-] = \sqrt{\frac{1.6 \times 10^{-5}}{1.0 \times 10^{-1}}} = 1.3 \times 10^{-2} M \qquad \text{(Eq. 15)}$$

If you want the precipitation to be 99.9% complete, then the Pb^{2+} ion concentration remaining in solution will be $1.0 \times 10^{-4} M$ and the Cl^- ion concentration will have to be raised to

$$[Cl^-] = \sqrt{\frac{1.6 \times 10^{-5}}{1.0 \times 10^{-4}}} = 0.40 M \qquad \text{(Eq. 16)}$$

With AgCl and Hg_2Cl_2, which are even less soluble, the precipitation of Ag^+ ion and Hg_2^{2+} ion as the chlorides will be even more than 99.9% complete.

In view of the common-ion effect, it may be tempting to add $12M$ HCl instead of $0.40M$ HCl to assure complete precipitation of the Group I cations. **Careful!** Not only might the soluble cation chlorides begin to precipitate, but the following subtle aspect of chemistry will become important in such a case.

Silver ion reacts with excess Cl^- ion to form a complex anion, dichloroargentate(I), $[AgCl_2]^-$, as shown in Equation 2.

$$Ag^+(aq) + 2Cl^-(aq) \rightleftharpoons [AgCl_2]^-(aq) \qquad \text{(Eq. 2)}$$
$$K = 1.0 \times 10^5$$

If the Cl^- ion concentration is raised too high, a considerable amount of the Ag^+ ion will be complexed as soluble $[AgCl_2]^-$ ion. This process is most conveniently considered as the redissolving of the AgCl precipitate. AgCl(s) is in equilibrium with its ions:

$$AgCl(s, white) \rightleftharpoons Ag^+(aq) + Cl^-(aq) \qquad \text{(Eq. 17)}$$
$$K_{sp} = 1.8 \times 10^{-10}$$

The formation of $[AgCl_2]^-$ ion does not occur appreciably at Cl^- ion concentrations of less than $5.0M$. We will use $6.0M$ HCl, which, through dilution and reaction, will yield a Cl^- ion concentration of $1-2M$ in the solution.

II. Separating Group II and III Cations

A further subdivision of the nine remaining cations in solution might be considered after Cl^- ion addition precipitates the Group I cations. A look at Table 3 reveals a rather large variation in the solubility product constants of the sulfides. The solubility product constants for these sulfides are small, indicating they are all very insoluble. The constants do fall into two groups on the basis of their magnitude. Separation of these cations is possible if we control reaction conditions, for example, by varying the S^{2-} ion concentration. The data in the last column, the S^{2-} ion concentration necessary to precipitate $0.10M$ cation, suggest that a separation might be possible by adjusting the S^{2-} ion concentration through control of the pH of the reaction. We must first consider the situation involving Fe^{3+} ion. In qualitative analysis schemes, iron is present as Fe^{3+} ion instead of iron(II) ion (Fe^{2+}, ferrous ion) to avoid the oxidation reduction reaction with Ag^+ ion as shown in Equation 18

$$Ag^+(aq) + Fe^{2+}(aq) \rightleftharpoons Ag(s, \text{gray}-\text{black}) + Fe^{3+}(aq) \qquad \text{(Eq. 18)}$$

After the precipitation of Ag^+ ion as AgCl, the addition of H_2S in acidic solution results in the reduction of Fe^{3+} ion to Fe^{2+} ion as shown in Equation 19.

$$2\,Fe^{3+}(aq) + S^{2-}(aq) \rightleftharpoons 2\,Fe^{2+}(aq) + S(s) \qquad \text{(Eq. 19)}$$

If we refer to Table 3 and neglect Fe^{3+} ion, which is converted to Fe^{2+} ion (See Equation 19), we can see that there is a large break in the S^{2-} ion concentration required to precipitate cations whose concentrations are $0.10M$. Cu^{2+}, Cd^{2+}, Bi^{3+}, and Sn^{4+} ions fall into one category and Fe^{2+} and Ni^{2+} ions fall into a second. The latter two cations require a much higher S^{2-} ion concentration for precipitation than the first four cations. The first four cations are from Group II, the **acid-insoluble sulfides**, and Fe^{2+} and Ni^{2+} ions are placed in the Group III category. When the S^{2-} ion concentration is controlled, the more insoluble metal sulfides (Group II cations) can be selectively precipitated while the Group III cations, the acid-soluble sulfides, remain in solution.

While the interesting details of this separation will be covered in other experiments, the general chemical principles involved will be illustrated in this experiment. To do so, we will use Cu^{2+} ion from Group II and Fe^{3+} ion from Group III. We will take advantage of the large difference in the soluzbility product constants of their sulfides to effect a separation of the two ions.

The first part of the experiment illustrates the separation of representative cations from Groups I, II, and III, Ag^+, Cu^{2+}, and Fe^{3+} ions. After carrying out this separation, we will use three important chemical reactions to identify the cations: (1) dithionite ion ($S_2O_4^{2-}$) as a strong reducing agent, (2) hexacyanoferrate(II) ion ($[Fe(CN)_6]^{4-}$, ferrocyanide ion) as a precipitating agent, and (3) thiocyanate ion (SCN^-) as a complexing agent. Dithionite ion is a strong reducing agent that reduces Ag^+ ion to elemental silver, $Ag(s)$, and sulfite ion (SO_3^{2-}) is formed as the oxidation product. Equation 20 shows the reduction of silver(I) in the ammonia complex ion diamminesilver(I), $[Ag(NH_3)_2]^+$, to $Ag(s)$.

$$2\,[Ag(NH_3)_2]^+(aq) + S_2O_4^{2-}(aq) + 2\,H_2O(l) \rightleftharpoons 2\,Ag(s, \text{gray}-\text{black}) + 2\,SO_3^{2-}(aq) + 4\,NH_4^+(aq) \quad \text{(Eq. 20)}$$

Elemental silver formed in this way appears gray–black in color.

The copper(II) sulfide (CuS, cupric sulfide) precipitate is dissolved in nitric acid (HNO_3), forming Cu^{2+} ion as shown in Equation 21.

$$3\,CuS(s) + 2\,HNO_3(aq) + 6\,H_3O^+(aq) \rightleftharpoons 3\,Cu^{2+}(aq) + 3\,S(s) + 2\,NO(aq) + 10\,H_2O(l) \qquad \text{(Eq. 21)}$$

Then, Cu^{2+} ion forms a dark blue complex ion, tetramminecopper(II), $[Cu(NH_3)_4]^{2+}$, with ammonia (NH_3) in basic solution as shown in Equation 22.

$$Cu^{2+}(aq) + 4\,NH_3(aq) \rightleftharpoons [Cu(NH_3)_4]^{2+}(aq, \text{dark blue}) \qquad \text{(Eq. 22)}$$

Adding acid shifts the equilibrium shown in Equation 22 by converting NH_3 to ammonium ion (NH_4^+). The presence of Cu^{2+} ion is detected by the addition of $[Fe(CN)_6]^{4-}$ ion, forming a reddish purple precipitate of copper hexacyanoferrate(II), $[Cu_2Fe(CN)_6]$, as shown in Equation 23.

$$2\,Cu^{2+}(aq) + [Fe(CN)_6]^{4-}(aq) \rightleftharpoons Cu_2Fe(CN)_6(s,\ reddish\ purple) \qquad (Eq.\ 23)$$

Iron(II) sulfide (FeS, ferrous sulfide) is also dissolved in HNO_3 during which process Fe^{2+} ion is oxidized to Fe^{3+} ion.

Thiocyanate ion (SCN^-) forms a stable complex with Fe^{3+} ion, as shown in Equation 24.

$$Fe^{3+}(aq) + SCN^-(aq) \rightleftharpoons [FeSCN]^{2+}(aq,\ deep\ red) \qquad (Eq.\ 24)$$
$$K = 1.0 \times 10^2$$

The thiocyanatoiron(III) complex ion ($[FeSCN]^{2+}$, ferrithiocyanate ion) imparts a deep red color to an aqueous solution. The formation of this complex upon addition of SCN^- ion is a sensitive test for the presence of Fe^{3+} ion.

III. Group I Cations (Insoluble Chlorides)

The problem remains of how to confirm definitely the presence of Ag^+, Pb^{2+} and Hg_2^{2+} ions, the Group I cations, in the chloride precipitate.

A. Separating and Confirming Lead(II)

Figure 1 shows the temperature dependence of the solubilities of the three chlorides. These curves suggest a procedure for further separation. In the

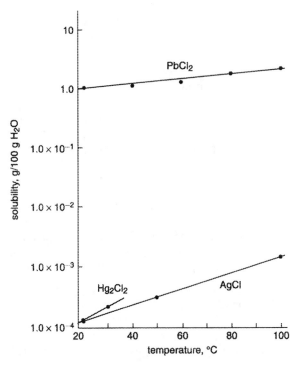

Figure 1
Effect of temperature on solubility of Group I cations

temperature range 20–100 °C, the solubilities of each of these chlorides increases, but to varying degrees. The approximate threefold increase in the solubility of $PbCl_2$ that occurs between 20 to 100 °C is such that at 100 °C appreciable amounts of $PbCl_2$ will dissolve, while $AgCl$ and Hg_2Cl_2 remain insoluble. Therefore, if the combined residues of the three chlorides are treated with hot water, the $PbCl_2$ should dissolve preferentially.

After any dissolved Pb^{2+} ion is separated by filtering the hot solution, the presence of Pb^{2+} ion may be confirmed by cooling the filtrate, resulting in the reprecipitation of any Pb^{2+} ion present as $PbCl_2$. If only a turbid solution results, the addition of HCl will precipitate more $PbCl_2$ if Pb^{2+} ion is present.

B. Separating Silver(I) and Mercury(I) and Confirming Mercury(I)

When separation of the remaining residue is attempted, a bit of chemical luck is encountered. A chemical reagent exists that preferentially acts to dissolve $AgCl$ and at the same time confirms the presence of Hg_2Cl_2. This reagent is aqueous NH_3. Silver ion forms a complex cation with NH_3

$$Ag^+(aq) + 2\ NH_3(aq) \rightleftharpoons [Ag(NH_3)_2]^+(aq) \tag{Eq. 25}$$

$$K = 1.5 \times 10^7$$

By combining Equation 17 and 25, the dissolution of solid $AgCl$ to form $[Ag(NH_3)_2]^+$ ion may be described with a single chemical equation

$$AgCl(s, white) + 2\ NH_3(aq) \rightleftharpoons [Ag(NH_3)_2]^+(aq) + Cl^-(aq) \tag{Eq. 26}$$

for which the equilibrium constant is

$$K = (1.5 \times 10^7)(1.8 \times 10^{-10}) = 2.7 \times 10^{-3} \tag{Eq. 27}$$

This equilibrium constant is a reasonably large one. Applying Le Châtelier's principle, we can shift the equilibrium to the right by adding excess aqueous NH_3, and virtually all of the $AgCl$ in the precipitate can be dissolved.

On the other hand, Hg_2Cl_2 reacts quite differently with aqueous NH_3. The following is an overall stoichiometric equation describing this reaction:

$$Hg_2Cl_2(s, white) + 2\,NH_3(aq) \rightleftharpoons HgNH_2Cl(s, white) + NH_4^+(aq) + Cl^-(aq) + Hg(l, black) \tag{Eq. 28}$$

Greater insight can be gained as to what is involved here if this equation is rewritten in a sequence of three equilibria, as shown in Equation 29, 30, and 31.

$$Hg_2Cl_2(s, white) \rightleftharpoons Hg_2^{2+}(aq) + 2\,Cl^-(aq) \tag{Eq. 29}$$

$$Hg_2^{2+}(aq) \rightleftharpoons Hg(l, black) + Hg^{2+}(aq) \tag{Eq. 30}$$

$$Hg^{2+}(aq) + 2\,NH_3(aq) + Cl^-(aq) \rightleftharpoons HgNH_2Cl(s, white) + NH_4^+(aq) \tag{Eq. 31}$$

The equilibrium in Equation 29 accounts for the presence of Hg_2^{2+} ion. As shown in Equation 30, the Hg_2^{2+} ion formed in the reaction shown in Equation 29 undergoes an autoredox or disproportionation reaction, in which Hg_2^{2+} ion is both oxidized to mercury(II) ion (Hg^{2+}, mercuric ion) and reduced to elemental mercury, $Hg(s)$. The addition of aqueous NH_3 in the presence of Cl^- ion converts the Hg^{2+} ion formed in Equation 29 to insoluble amidochloromercury(II) ($HgNH_2Cl$), as shown in Equation 31. Hence, the addition of aqueous NH_3 to solid Hg_2Cl_2 will shift the equilibrium in Equation 29, 30, and 31 to the right, resulting in the conversion of Hg_2Cl_2 to $Hg(s)$ and $HgNH_2Cl$. The very low solubility of $HgNH_2Cl$ is the driving force behind this sequence of reactions. Elemental mercury appears black when finely divided, and $HgNH_2Cl$ is white. The total precipitate appears to have a black or gray color, thus confirming the presence of Hg_2^{2+} ion in the original solution.

C. Confirming Silver(I)

Silver ion is now present as $[Ag(NH_3)_2]^+$ ion in solution with Cl^- ion, the latter formed from the dissolution of $AgCl$, as shown in Equation 26.

In aqueous solution, NH_3 is a Brønsted base.

$$NH_3(aq) + H_2O(l) \rightleftharpoons NH_4^+(aq) + OH^-(aq) \qquad \text{(Eq. 32)}$$
$$K_b = 1.8 \times 10^{-5}$$

Equations can be written for the simultaneous equilibria relevant to the Ag^+ ion confirmation in the following sequence of two reactions:

$$[Ag(NH_3)_2]^+(aq) \rightleftharpoons Ag^+(aq) + 2\,NH_3(aq) \qquad \text{(Eq. 33)}$$
$$K = 6.7 \times 10^{-8}$$

$$OH^-(aq) + H_3O^+(aq) \rightleftharpoons 2\,H_2O(l) \qquad \text{(Eq. 34)}$$
$$K = 1.0 \times 10^{14}$$

As a result of the equilibrium in Equation 33, some NH_3 is present in solution. The reaction of NH_3 formed in Equation 33 with water forms NH_4^+ and OH^- ions, as shown in Equation 32. The OH^- ion formed in Equation 32 will react with H_3O^+ ion to form water, as shown in Equation 34. Thus, the addition of acid to a solution containing $[Ag(NH_3)_2]^+$ ion will shift all three equilibria to the right, resulting in the release of Ag^+ ion into the solution.

With the Cl^- ion already present, if the volume of the solution has not been increased too much, the ion product of Ag^+ ion and Cl^- ion will exceed the solubility product constant of $AgCl$. White $AgCl$ will precipitate; the formation of this precipitate confirms the presence of Ag^+ ion in the original solution.

In this experiment, you will separate Ag^+, Cu^{2+}, and Fe^{3+} ions from a known solution and verify the presence of each cation by a confirmation test. Then, you will separate Ag^+, Hg_2^{2+}, and Pb^{2+} ions (Group I cations) from a second known solution and verify the presence of each cation by a confirmation test. Finally, you will determine the cations present in an unknown solution containing one or more of the Group I cations, using the same procedure as you did with the known cation solution.

PROCEDURE

Some Notes on Semimicro Technique

1. *Precipitations:* The precipitating reagent should be added dropwise with stirring until precipitation is complete.

2. *Completeness of Precipitation:* So that interfering cations are not left in solution, it is often necessary, where noted, to allow the precipitate to settle in the test tube, or to centrifuge the supernatant liquid and the precipitate, and then carefully add 1 additional drop of reagent. If more precipitate forms, a few more drops of reagent should be added and the above procedure repeated until no further precipitation is observed.

3. *Washing Precipitates:* To ensure removal of interfering ions from moist precipitates, it is necessary, where noted, to wash the precipitate. This procedure involves decanting the supernatant liquid, adding the required amount of specified wash liquid to the tube containing the moist precipitate, mixing the precipitate and wash liquid thoroughly with a clean glass stirring rod, centrifuging, and decanting and discarding the wash liquid.

CAUTION

A solution in a small test tube cannot be heated safely over a direct flame.

4. *Heating a Solution:* Placing the test tube containing the solution to be heated in a hot or boiling water bath is generally a preferred method.

5. *Removing Supernatant Liquids:* Liquids over precipitates are most often removed by careful decantation. However, the supernatant liquid can carefully be withdrawn with a small medicine dropper or pipet, if necessary.

Occasionally a precipitate does not centrifuge completely. To fully separate a supernatant liquid in such a situation, twist a small piece of cotton batting to a point and insert it partway into the tip of a clear eyedropper, leaving a tuft extending outside the tip. Draw up the supernatant liquid through the cotton, which will filter out the floating particles of precipitate. Enough precipitate should remain in the test tube for testing of those cations. Carefully remove the cotton and release the clear supernatant liquid into a clean 10×75-mm test tube.

CHEMICAL ALERT

6M acetic acid—toxic and corrosive
6M ammonia—toxic, corrosive, and irritant
0.1M copper(II) nitrate in 0.1M HNO$_3$—toxic, irritant, and oxidant
6M hydrochloric acid—toxic and corrosive
0.1M iron(III) nitrate in 0.1M HNO$_3$—toxic, corrosive, and oxidant
0.1M lead(II) nitrate in 0.1M HNO$_3$—toxic, irritant, and oxidant
0.1M mercury(I) nitrate in 0.1M HNO$_3$—highly toxic and oxidant
6M nitric acid—toxic, corrosive, and strong oxidant
0.1M potassium ferrocyanide—irritant
0.1M potassium thiocyanate—irritant
0.1M silver nitrate in 0.1M HNO$_3$—toxic, corrosive, and oxidant
sodium dithionite—toxic and irritant
1M thioacetamide—toxic and carcinogen

CAUTION

Wear departmentally approved eye protection while doing this experiment.

I. Separating Selected Group I Cations from Group II and III Cations

A. Precipitating Group I Cations (Insoluble Chlorides)

In a clean appropriate container, obtain from your laboratory instructor a known solution that is approximately $0.1M$ in each of the three cations, Ag^+, Cu^{2+}, and Fe^{3+} ions. With a clean dropper, transfer 15 drops of this mixture to a 75-mm test tube.

CAUTION

$6M$ hydrochloric acid is a corrosive, toxic solution that can cause burns. Prevent contact with your eyes, skin, and clothing. Avoid inhaling vapors and ingesting the solution.

From a second clean dropper, add dropwise $6M$ HCl to the mixture in the test tube, while stirring, until the precipitation is complete.

Record all observations on Data Sheet 1.

Place the tube containing the mixture in the centrifuge and balance it with another tube containing an amount of water equal to the volume of the mixture in the tube. Centrifuge for 2 min. Decant the supernatant liquid, containing Group II and III cations, from the precipitate into a clean, dry test tube. Label this tube and retain it for future use.

Wash the precipitate in the test tube with 2 mL of distilled or deionized water. Thoroughly stir the contents of the tube using a clean glass stirring rod. Centrifuge the mixture in the tube for 2 min.

NOTE: In all parts of this experiment, follow the directions of your laboratory instructor for discarding reaction mixtures and unused reagents.

Decant the supernatant liquid from the precipitate and discard the supernatant liquid.

CAUTION

$6M$ ammonia is a corrosive, toxic solution. Prevent contact with your eyes, skin, and clothing. Avoid inhaling vapors and ingesting the solution.

Add 15 drops of $6M$ NH$_3$ to dissolve the precipitate. Add a small amount, about the size of a grain of rice, of solid sodium dithionite to the solution in the tube. Record all observations on Data Sheet 1.

B. Precipitating Group II Cations as Sulfides from Acidic H$_2$S Solution

Estimate the pH of the original supernatant liquid retained from the previous Group I precipitation by using short-range pH paper supplied by your laboratory instructor. If the pH of the supernatant liquid is not within

±0.3 pH unit of a pH of 0.5, adjust the pH of the solution to approximately 0.5 by adding dropwise from a clean dropper either $0.5M$ HCl or $0.5M$ NH$_3$, as appropriate. Prepare the $0.5M$ solutions by diluting 1 drop of a $6M$ solution with 11 drops of distilled water and thoroughly mixing with a clean glass stirring rod. This pH adjustment is important. If the pH is too low, that is, if the hydrogen ion concentration is too high, the concentration of S^{2-} ion will be insufficient to permit the precipitation of CuS. If the pH is too high, CuS and FeS will both precipitate.

CAUTION

Thioacetamide has been demonstrated to be a carcinogen in animal feeding studies. It is safe to use when handled prudently. Avoid skin contact with the thioacetamide solution. Wash your hands thoroughly with soap or detergent after using the solution.

When you have properly adjusted the pH of the supernatant liquid, use a clean dropper to add 10 drops of $1M$ thioacetamide solution to the solution in the test tube. Heat the tube and its contents in a boiling water bath for 5 min.

Record all observations on Data Sheet 1.

Centrifuge the tube and its contents for 2 min. Decant the supernatant liquid into another clean 75-mm test tube. Label these tubes. Retain the tube containing the CuS precipitate and the tube containing the supernatant liquid.

Test the supernatant liquid for completeness of precipitation by adding 5 drops of $1M$ thioacetamide to the solution. Heat the tube and its contents in a boiling water bath for 5 min. If additional dark-colored precipitate forms, the first CuS precipitation was not complete. A light-colored precipitate may form, which is elemental sulfur formed from the decomposition of thioacetamide.

Centrifuge the tube containing the supernatant liquid. Decant the supernatant liquid into a clean 75-mm test tube and discard any precipitate that may have formed. Label the tube and retain the supernatant liquid for Group III tests.

CAUTION

$6M$ nitric acid is a corrosive, toxic solution that can cause severe burns. Prevent contact with your eyes, skin, and clothing, and combustible material. Avoid inhaling vapors and ingesting the solution.

Add 20 drops of $6M$ HNO$_3$ to the tube containing the original CuS precipitate. Carefully heat the tube and its contents in a boiling water bath while carefully stirring the mixture with a clean glass stirring rod to suspend the CuS precipitate in the $6M$ HNO$_3$. Continue heating for 3 min.

Centrifuge the warm tube and its contents, if necessary, to facilitate the removal of any undissolved material. Decant the supernatant liquid into a 75-mm test tube and discard any precipitate. Let the tube and its contents cool. Add $6M$ NH$_3$ dropwise until the solution is just basic to litmus paper. Then add 5 more drops of $6M$ NH$_3$ in excess.

CAUTION ⚠️

6*M* acetic acid is a corrosive solution that can cause burns. Prevent contact with your eyes, skin, and clothing. Avoid inhaling the vapors and ingesting the solution.

Add 6*M* acetic acid (HOAc) dropwise until the solution is just acidic to litmus paper. Add 5 drops of 0.1*M* potassium hexacyanoferrate(ll), [$K_4Fe(CN)_6$], solution. Stir the solution with a clean glass stirring rod.

Record all observations on Data Sheet 1.

C. Precipitating Group III Cations as Sulfides from Alkaline H_2S Solution

Select the labeled test tube containing the supernatant liquid from the Group II precipitation. Add 6*M* NH_3 dropwise with stirring until the solution is just basic to litmus paper. Then add 7 drops of 6*M* NH_3 in excess. The solution should now be strongly basic. If there is residual H_2S in solution and Fe^{2+} is present, a black precipitate of FeS will form as the solution becomes more basic.

To complete the formation of the FeS precipitate, add 10 drops of 1*M* thioacetamide to the basic solution. Thoroughly stir the mixture with a clean glass stirring rod. Warm the tube and its contents in a boiling water bath for 5 min.

Centrifuge the tube and its contents for 2 min. Decant the supernatant liquid from the precipitate and discard the supernatant liquid.

Using a clean dropper, add 15 drops of 6*M* HNO_3 to the precipitate. Thoroughly stir the mixture with a clean glass stirring rod. Heat the tube and its contents in a boiling water bath for 5 min. If the solution is cloudy, centrifuge the tube and its contents for 2 min. Using a clean dropper, add 3 drops of 0.1*M* potassium thiocyanate (KSCN) to the clear solution in the tube.

Record all observations on Data Sheet 1.

II. Precipitating Group I Cations, Silver(I), Mercury(I), and Lead(II)

A flowchart is given in Figure 2 for the separation and identification of the Group I cations Ag^+, Hg_2^{2+} and Pb^{2+}.

Obtain a known mixture containing the Group I cations from your laboratory instructor. Using a clean dropper, transfer 15 drops of the known solution to a clean 75-mm test tube. Using another clean dropper, add sufficient 6*M* HCl dropwise with shaking to effect complete precipitation. Centrifuge the tube and its contents for 2 min. Add 1 drop of 6*M* HCl to the mixture. If additional precipitate forms, centrifuge the tube and its contents again for 2 min. Retest the mixture for completeness of precipitation. When precipitation is complete, decant the supernatant liquid from the precipitate.

If only Group I cations were present in the original sample solution, discard the supernatant liquid. If the sample solution is to be analyzed for Group II, III, and/or IV cations, retain and label the supernatant liquid.

Retain the precipitate in the tube for use in the next section.

Record all observations on Data Sheet 2.

A. Separating and Confirming Lead(II)

Add 2 mL of distilled water to the Group I precipitate in the test tube. While stirring with a clean glass stirring rod, heat the tube and its contents in a

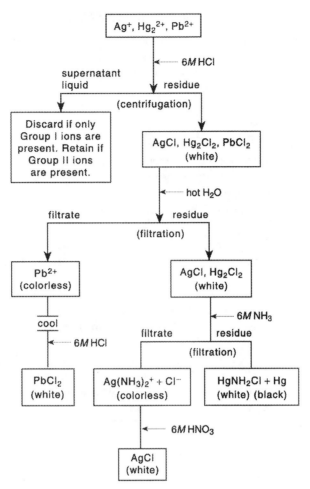

Figure 2
Group I flowchart

boiling water bath for 3 min. While heating the Group I precipitate, heat 4 mL of distilled water in a separate test tube in the boiling water bath. Heat another 10 mL of distilled water for later use. Pour 4 mL of hot distilled water through the filter paper immediately prior to filtering the precipitate. Discard this water. By heating the filter paper and the funnel, any dissolved Pb^{2+} ion will probably not reprecipitate during filtration. Thoroughly stir the Group I precipitate in the hot water. Rapidly filter the hot solution through the warmed funnel and filter paper. Retain the filtrate in a clean test tube.

Place the funnel in a large test tube. Wash the residue with two 5-mL portions of hot distilled water. Discard the washings. Leave the residue on the filter paper in the funnel and retain the residue for further analysis in the next section of this experiment.

Cool the filtrate in the test tube by immersing the tube in cold water. If there is any question as to the results, add 2–3 drops of 6M HCl to the cooled filtrate. Thoroughly stir the mixture in the tube with a clean glass stirring rod.

Record all observations on Data Sheet 2.

B. Separating and Confirming Mercury(I)

Place a small test tube under the funnel containing the residue from the previous filtration. Using a clean dropper, add 2 mL of $6M$ NH_3 dropwise to the residue on the filter paper. Retain the filtrate for confirmation of the presence of Ag^+ ion.

Record all observations on Data Sheet 2.

C. Confirming Silver(I)

Add $6M$ HNO_3 from a clean dropper to the test tube containing the ammonia filtrate, with stirring, until the solution is acidic when tested with litmus paper.

Record all observations on Data Sheet 2.

III. Analyzing a Group I Unknown Cation Solution

Obtain an unknown solution containing one or more of the Group I cations from your laboratory instructor. Record the unknown identification number on Data Sheet 3.

Repeat the procedure in Part II with this solution. List on Data Sheet 3 the cations you find in your unknown solution. Cite evidence on Data Sheet 3 proving the presence of the cations you report.

CAUTION

Wash your hands thoroughly with soap or detergent before leaving the laboratory.

_____   _____   _____

Post-Laboratory Questions

(Use the spaces provided for the answers and additional paper if necessary.)

1. What are the properties of the Group I, II, and III cations that permit their separation by groups?

2. (1) What is the electron configuration of Hg^+ ion?

(2) Why does it actually exist as Hg_2^{2+} ion rather than as Hg^+ ion?

(3) When Hg_2^{2+} ion disproportionates, why does it become $Hg(s)$ and Hg^{2+} ion rather than form species with some other oxidation numbers?

3. FeS(s) dissolves by the addition of HNO_3 in a manner similar to that of CuS(s). In the process, the Fe^{2+} ion is oxidized to Fe^{3+} ion. Write an equation for this reaction.

4. A student mistakenly added concentrated (12M) HCl to a sample of unknown, instead of adding 6M HCl, as directed.

    (1) At first, a large amount of light-colored precipitate formed, but some dissolved on further addition of concentrated HCl. Write an equation(s) for the reaction(s) that might have occurred.

    (2) The precipitate was separated from the supernatant liquid in (1) and was found to be insoluble in hot water. The precipitate turned grey-black upon addition of 6M NH$_3$. The student concluded that the unknown contained Hg$_2^{2+}$ ion. The student received a low mark on the experiment, because the unknown actually contained all three Group I cations. Explain what happened.

5. Many of the reactions utilized in this laboratory experiment involve substances with small solubility product constants. AgCl is one such substance. Nevertheless, a precipitate of AgCl will dissolve in either 6M HCl or 6M NH$_3$.

    (1) Briefly explain why each of these reagents dissolves AgCl(s). Write appropriate equations to support your answer.

    (2) Briefly explain why it is possible to reprecipitate AgCl(s) by adding HCl to [Ag(NH$_3$)$_2$]$^+$ ion but not by adding ammonia to [AgCl$_2$]$^-$ ion. Write appropriate equations to support your answer.

Name   *Section*   *Date*

Data Sheet 1

(Record below all observations made while performing Section I of this experiment.)

I. Separating Selected Group I Cations from Group II and III Cations

A. Precipitating Group I cations

B. Precipitating Group II cations as sulfides

C. Precipitating Group III cations as sulfides

Data Sheet 2

(Record below all observations made while performing Section II of this experiment.)

II. Precipitating Group I Cations, Silver(I), Mercury(I), and Lead(II)

A. Separating and confirming lead(II)

B. Separating and confirming mercury(I)

C. Confirming silver(I)

Data Sheet 3

III. Analyzing a Group I Unknown Cation Solution

unknown identification number _____

cations found _____

_____

_____

Present evidence proving the presence of listed cations.

Name   *Section*   *Date*

Pre-Laboratory Assignment

1. Read an authoritative source for a discussion of the techniques to be used in this experiment.

2. Qualitative analysis studies require the use of a large number of chemical reagents, each of which must be treated with care. To illustrate this statement, list the reagents used to determine and confirm the presence of Ag^+ ion in a sample, and describe the safety problems associated with each.

3. Using your chemistry text or a dictionary as a reference, define the following terms as they pertain to this experiment.

(1) qualitative analysis

(2) precipitate

(3) supernatant liquid

(4) solubility

(5) Le Châtelier's principle

4. Write chemical equations for the following reactions.

(1) $AgCl(s) + NH_3(aq)$

(2) $Hg_2Cl_2(s) + NH_3(aq)$

Explain how adding aqueous NH_3 to the combined $AgCl-Hg_2Cl_2$ precipitate effects the separation of the two cations.

5. For a solution containing at least one of the cations involved in this experiment, answer the following questions.

   (1) When 6*M* HCl is added to the solution, a white precipitate forms. What cation(s) may be present in the solution?

   (2) When hot water is added to the precipitate, a white solid remains after filtration. What cation(s) may be present?

   (3) When the filtrate from (2) is cooled, a white precipitate forms. What cation(s) may be present?

   (4) When the precipitate remaining in (2) after filtration is treated with aqueous NH_3, the precipitate completely dissolves. What conclusions can be drawn about the presence or absence of the cation(s) in the solution?

   (5) If HNO_3 is added to the solution in (4), what would you expect to happen? Briefly explain.

6. (1) At what pH will FeS begin to precipitate if the Fe^{2+} ion concentration is $0.1M$ and the H_2S concentration is $0.01M$? Show all calculations to support your answer.

(2) At what pH will CuS begin to precipitate if the Cu^{2+} ion concentration is $0.1M$ and the H_2S concentration is $0.01M$? Show all calculations to support your answer.

The Chemistry and Qualitative Analysis of Cations: Group II

*Prepared by James G. Boyles, Bates College, and
Judith C. Foster and David S. Page, Bowdoin College*

PURPOSE OF THE EXPERIMENT

Develop the chemistry of the selected Group II cations (Bi^{3+}, Cu^{2+}, Cd^{2+}, and Sn^{4+} ions). Use this chemistry to establish a procedure for verifying qualitatively the presence of these selected cations.

BACKGROUND INFORMATION

A selected group of chemically important and commonly encountered cations appear in Table 1 on the next page. Of these cations, Ag^+, Hg_2^{2+}, and Pb^{2+} ions, the so-called Group I cations, can be separated from the others by precipitation as chlorides.

I. Separating Group II Cations

Nine cations remain in solution after the Group I cations are removed. Four of these, Bi^{3+}, Cu^{2+}, Cd^{2+}, and Sn^{4+} ions, can be selectively precipitated as the sulfides. These four cations are known as Group II cations. The selective precipitation is accomplished by controlling the sulfide ion (S^{2-}) concentration in the solution. After we separate these Group II cations from the other cations, we can take advantage of the unique chemical properties of each cation to verify its presence.

II. Precipitating Group II Sulfides (Bi_2S_3, CuS, CdS, and SnS_2)

The data in Table 2 on the next page show that the sulfides of both Group II and III cations are very insoluble. Closer examination shows that the Group II sulfide cations are considerably less soluble than those of Group III. If precipitation conditions are carefully controlled, separation of cations of the two groups can be achieved. The condition most easily controlled is the S^{2-} ion concentration.

Table 2 reveals that precipitating the $0.1M$ cations iron(II) (Fe^{2+}, ferrous) and nickel(II) (Ni^{2+}, nickelous) as sulfides requires a S^{2-} ion concentration that is at least 1×10^6 times larger than that required for precipitating Bi^{3+}, Cu^{2+}, Cd^{2+}, and Sn^{4+} ions as their respective sulfides. Furthermore, the sulfides of Cr^{3+}, Ba^{2+}, and Ca^{2+} ions are not stable in aqueous solution.

Table 1 *Nomenclature and formulas of some cations*

cation	common name	formula
barium		Ba^{2+}
bismuth(III)		Bi^{3+}
calcium		Ca^{2+}
cadmium(II)		Cd^{2+}
chromium(III)	chromic	Cr^{3+}
copper(II)	cupric	Cu^{2+}
iron(III)	ferric	Fe^{3+}
lead(II)	plumbous	Pb^{2+}
mercury(I)	mercurous	Hg_2^{2+}
nickel(II)	nickelous	Ni^{2+}
silver(I)		Ag^+
tin(IV)	stannic	Sn^{4+}

Thus, a separation of these Group II cations appears possible through sulfide precipitation.

When an acidic solution containing iron(III) ion (Fe^{3+}, ferric ion) is treated with hydrogen sulfide (H_2S), Fe^{3+} ion is reduced to Fe^{2+} ion, as shown in Equation 1.

$$2\,Fe^{3+}(aq) + H_2S(aq) + 2\,H_2O(l) \rightleftharpoons 2\,Fe^{2+}(aq) + S(s) + 2\,H_3O^+(aq) \qquad \text{(Eq. 1)}$$

Thus, in acidic solutions of H_2S, the iron chemistry of concern is that of the +2 oxidation state, Fe^{2+} ion.

Table 2 *Solubility product constants at 25 °C of various cations*

ion	chloride	sulfide	minimum $[S^{2-}]$ needed to precipitate 0.1M cations
Group I			
Ag^+	1.8×10^{-10}	6.8×10^{-50}	—
Hg_2^{2+}	1.3×10^{-18}	5.8×10^{-44}	—
Pb^{2+}	1.6×10^{-5}	8.4×10^{-28}	—
Group II			
Cu^{2+}	$>10^{-1}$ (soluble)	8.7×10^{-36}	8.7×10^{-35}
Cd^{2+}	$>10^{-1}$ (soluble)	7.8×10^{-27}	7.8×10^{-26}
Bi^{3+}	unstable (soluble)	6.8×10^{-97}	4.1×10^{-32}
Sn^{4+}	soluble	$SnS_2 = 1.0 \times 10^{-70}$	3.2×10^{-35}
Group III			
Fe^{2+}	soluble	$FeS = 4.9 \times 10^{-18}$	4.9×10^{-17}
Fe^{3+}	soluble	$Fe_2S_3 = 1.0 \times 10^{-88*}$	$2.2 \times 10^{-29*}$
Ni^{2+}	soluble	$NiS = 1.8 \times 10^{-21}$	1.8×10^{-20}
Cr^{3+}	soluble	not stable in H_2O	—
Group IV			
Ba^{2+}	soluble	not stable in H_2O	—
Ca^{2+}	soluble	not stable in H_2O	—

*Fe_2S_3 in acid decomposes to FeS and S.

Fe^{2+} and Ni^{2+} ions can be separated from the Group II cations. The S^{2-} ion concentration that must be exceeded before the most insoluble sulfide of the two, nickel(ll) sulfide (NiS, nickelous sulfide), begins to precipitate can be calculated as follows.

The dissolution of NiS is represented by Equation 2.

$$NiS(s, black) \rightleftharpoons Ni^{2+}(aq) + S^{2-}(aq) \qquad \text{(Eq. 2)}$$

The K_{sp} expression for NiS is:

$$K_{sp} = [Ni^{2+}][S^{2-}] = 1.8 \times 10^{-21} \qquad \text{(Eq. 3)}$$

If the concentration of Ni^{2+} ion in solution is assumed to be 0.10M, the S^{2-} ion concentration just sufficient to allow precipitation of NiS may be found using Equation 4.

$$[S^{2-}] = \frac{1.8 \times 10^{-21}}{0.10} = 1.8 \times 10^{-20} M \qquad \text{(Eq. 4)}$$

Thus, the precipitation of NiS and iron(II) sulfide (FeS, ferrous sulfide), with their larger solubility product constants, can be *avoided* if the S^{2-} ion concentration is maintained below $1.8 \times 10^{-20} M$. Is this S^{2-} ion concentration large enough to precipitate the Group II cations?

Consider the most soluble of the Group II sulfides, cadmium(II) sulfide (CdS). The dissolution of CdS is represented by Equation 5.

$$CdS(s) \rightleftharpoons Cd^{2+}(aq) + S^{2-}(aq) \qquad \text{(Eq. 5)}$$

The K_{sp} expression for CdS is:

$$K_{sp} = [Cd^{2+}][S^{2-}] = 7.8 \times 10^{-27} \qquad \text{(Eq. 6)}$$

When the S^{2-} ion concentration is $1.8 \times 10^{-20} M$, the concentration of Cd^{2+} ion that remains in solution may be found using Equation 7.

$$[Cd^{2+}] = \frac{7.8 \times 10^{-27}}{1.8 \times 10^{-20}} = 4.3 \times 10^{-7} M \qquad \text{(Eq. 7)}$$

Therefore, we can see that in a $1.8 \times 10^{-20} M$ solution of S^{2-} ion, the Cd^{2+} ion concentration at equilibrium will be $4.3 \times 10^{-7} M$. If the original solution of cations is 0.10M in each cation, only 4.3×10^{-4}% of the original amount of Cd^{2+} ion will remain in solution. In other words, even for the most soluble sulfide of Group II, the precipitation will be more than 99.9995% complete at the designated S^{2-} ion concentration. This degree of precipitation is more than adequate for qualitative work. The key to separating the Group II cations is establishing a S^{2-} ion concentration of approximately $1.8 \times 10^{-20} M$.

On the basis of the overall equilibrium shown in Equation 8

$$H_2S(aq) + 2 H_2O(l) \rightleftharpoons 2 H_3O^+(aq) + S^{2-}(aq) \qquad \text{(Eq. 8)}$$

it can be shown that the S^{2-} ion concentration is inversely proportional to the square of the hydronium ion (H$_3$O$^+$) concentration.

$$K_{H_2S} = \frac{[H_3O^+]^2[S^{2-}]}{[H_2S]} = 1.3 \times 10^{-20} \qquad \text{(Eq. 9)}$$

$$[S^{2-}] = \frac{(1.3 \times 10^{-20})[H_2S]}{[H_3O^+]^2} \qquad \text{(Eq. 10)}$$

When the H_3O^+ ion concentration, or operationally the pH, of a solution containing H_2S is controlled, the S^{2-} ion concentration can be controlled. A more complete discussion of acid–base sulfide equilibria is given in **ANAL 364, The Chemistry and Qualitative Analysis of Cations: Group Separations and Separation of Group I Cations,** in this series.

Gaseous H_2S is very toxic. The use of commercial H_2S gas as the sulfide source in this experiment would result in large releases of H_2S, which is not safe. Instead, we will use thioacetamide (CH_3CSNH_2) as a convenient *in situ* source of H_2S. When thioacetamide dissolves in aqueous solution, the equilibrium shown in Equation 11 is established

$$
\underset{\substack{|| \\ O}}{\overset{\substack{S \\ ||}}{CH_3-C-NH_2}}(aq) + 2\,H_2O(l) \rightleftharpoons
$$

$$CH_3C-O^-(aq) + NH_4^+(aq) + H_2S(g) \qquad \text{(Eq. 11)}$$

The forward reaction in this equilibrium is endothermic. Therefore, when the solution is heated, this system can be shifted to a new equilibrium position involving a higher concentration of products, as would be predicted from Le Châtelier's principle. When $1.0M$ thioacetamide solution is heated to 100 °C, the reaction in Equation 11 occurs, and a solution of approximately $1.0 \times 10^{-2}M$ H_2S results. Table 3 gives the equilibrium concentration of S^{2-} ion in such solutions at various H_3O^+ ion concentrations. If the solution is maintained at a pH of 1 or slightly less, the desired S^{2-} ion concentration in solution will be established, that is, approximately $1.8 \times 10^{-20}M$. This concentration is sufficient to precipitate the Group II cations but not the other Group III and IV cations.

Next, we will consider the chemistry of the individual Group II cations (Bi^{3+}, Cu^{2+}, Cd^{2+}, and Sn^{4+} ions) in order to develop procedures to confirm their presence in aqueous solution.

A. Separating and Confirming Tin(IV)

Of the four Group II sulfides, only tin(IV) sulfide (SnS_2, stannic sulfide) is soluble in excess concentrated potassium hydroxide (KOH). The reaction

Table 3 *Equilibrium concentrations of sulfide ion in $1.0 \times 10^{-2}M$ H_2S solutions of various H_3O^+ ion concentrations*

solutions	pH	S^{2-} ion concentration mol L^{-1}
$1.0 \times 10^{-2}M$ H_2S	4.5	1.3×10^{-13}
$1.0 \times 10^{-2}M$ $H_2S + 1.0 \times 10^{-3}M$ H_3O^+(aq)	3	1.3×10^{-16}
$1.0 \times 10^{-2}M$ $H_2S + 1.0 \times 10^{-2}M$ H_3O^+(aq)	2	1.3×10^{-18}
$1.0 \times 10^{-2}M$ $H_2S + 0.10M$ H_3O^+(aq)	1	1.3×10^{-20}
$1.0 \times 10^{-2}M$ $H_2S + 1.00M$ H_3O^+(aq)	0	1.3×10^{-22}

occurs because of the amphoteric nature of SnS_2, its ability to act as both an acid and a base. In this experiment, as shown in Equation 12, SnS_2 acts as an acid, binding OH^- ion. Only tin(IV) sulfide (SnS_2, stannic sulfide) is soluble in excess concentrated potassium hydroxide (KOH), forming the complex ions hexahydroxostannate(IV), $[Sn(OH)_6]^{2-}$, and trisulfidostannate(IV), $[SnS_3]^{2-}$.

$$3\,SnS_2(s,\text{ yellow}) + 6\,OH^-(aq) \rightleftharpoons [Sn(OH)_6]^{2-}(aq) + 2\,[SnS_3]^{2-} \qquad \text{(Eq. 12)}$$

The other Group II cations do not behave in this manner. The result is that the supernatant liquid contains the two dissolved tin species, and the other Group II sulfides remain in the precipitate.

After the supernatant liquid containing the $[Sn(OH)_6]^{2-}$ and $[SnS_3]^{2-}$ ions is separated from the undissolved sulfide precipitate containing CdS, copper(II) sulfide (CuS, cupric sulfide), and bismuth sulfide (Bi_2S_3), the complexes can be destroyed through the addition of acid, which reverses the reaction shown in Equation 12.

Due to possible oxidation of sulfide, S^{2-} ion might have to be added to confirm the presence of tin(IV) ion (Sn^{4+}, stannic) by observing the formation of a yellow to yellow-brown precipitate of SnS_2. In the laboratory, you should take care to avoid confusing the SnS_2 precipitate with a whitish yellow precipitate of colloidal sulfur, which may form as a result of the air oxidation of H_2S, as shown in Equation 13. If you are unsure at this point, you may add excess OH^- ion again. If the precipitate is SnS_2, it will dissolve, but if it is sulfur, it will not dissolve.

$$2\,H_2S(aq) + O_2(g) \rightarrow 2\,S(s,\text{ whitish-yellow}) + 2\,H_2O(l) \qquad \text{(Eq. 13)}$$

B. Separating and Confirming Cadmium(II)

The remaining precipitate contains CdS, CuS, and Bi_2S_3. The addition of H_3O^+ ion alone is sufficient to shift the equilibria of both Equations 14 and 15 to the right: CdS is dissolved and separated from the other sulfides.

$$CdS(s,\text{ yellow-orange}) \rightleftharpoons Cd^{2+}(aq) + S^{2-}(aq) \qquad \text{(Eq. 14)}$$

$$S^{2-}(aq) + 2\,H_3O^+(aq) \rightleftharpoons H_2S(aq) + 2\,H_2O(l) \qquad \text{(Eq. 15)}$$

A $1.0M$ solution of hot hydrochloric acid (HCl) will selectively dissolve the CdS from the mixed precipitate. The relatively high chloride ion (Cl^-) concentration causes the equilibrium of yet a third reaction (See Equation 16) to shift to the right, which favors the formation of tetrachlorocadminate(II) ion, $[CdCl_4]^{2-}$, shifting the equilibrium of Equation 14 even further to the right.

$$Cd^{2+}(aq) + 4\,Cl^-(aq) \rightleftharpoons [CdCl_4]^{2-}(aq) \qquad \text{(Eq. 16)}$$

CuS and Bi_2S_3 will not dissolve in the presence of H_3O^+ ion alone. The S^{2-} ion concentrations needed to precipitate CuS and Bi_2S_3 are, respectively, 10^9 and 10^6 times smaller than that for CdS; thus it is more difficult to dissolve these sulfides. In addition, Cu^{2+} ion forms only a very weak complex with Cl^- ion, and Bi^{3+} ion does not form any stable chloride complex. Thus, when $1.0M$ HCl is added to the mixed precipitate, CdS can be selectively dissolved. The mixture is then centrifuged. The supernatant liquid is tested for the presence of Cd^{2+} ion by making the solution basic to shift the equilibria in Equations 14, 15, and 16 to the left. If Cd^{2+} ion is present, a yellow precipitate of CdS will form.

C. Separating and Confirming Bismuth(III) and Copper(II)

The precipitate containing the very insoluble CuS and Bi_2S_3 can only be dissolved by the use of a strong oxidizing agent. Nitrate ion (NO_3^-) is a good oxidizing agent and in hot solution will readily oxidize S^{2-} ion to elemental sulfur, S(s). The dissolution of CuS may be represented by the equilibria in Equations 17 and 18.

$$3\,CuS(s, black) \rightleftharpoons 3\,Cu^{2+}(aq) + 3\,S^{2-}(aq) \qquad \text{(Eq. 17)}$$

$$3\,S^{2-}(aq) + 2\,NO_3^-(aq) + 8\,H_3O^+(aq) \rightleftharpoons 3\,S(s, yellow) + 2\,NO(aq) + 12\,H_2O(l) \qquad \text{(Eq. 18)}$$

Similar equilibria apply to the dissolution of Bi_2S_3. Under these conditions, the redox reaction shown in Equation 18 is sufficiently complete to shift the equilibria in Equations 17 and 18 to the right, thus dissolving the solid CuS. A similar process occurs with the equilibrium for Bi_2S_3. Heating also facilitates the dissolution by decreasing the solubility of nitrogen(II) oxide (NO, nitrogen monoxide or nitric oxide) in the solution. Thus, the NO concentration is lowered and the equilibria in both Equations 17 and 18 shifts to the right. Although NO is colorless, a red-brown colored gas may be seen coming from the solution at this point, because NO reacts very rapidly with oxygen to form red-brown nitrogen(IV) oxide (NO_2, nitrogen dioxide), as shown in Equation 19.

$$2\,NO(g) + O_2(g) \rightleftharpoons 2\,NO_2(g, red\text{-}brown) \qquad \text{(Eq. 19)}$$

Following dissolution of CuS and Bi_2S_3 in hot nitric acid (HNO_3), addition of aqueous ammonia (NH_4OH) to this solution, which now contains Bi^{3+} and Cu^{2+} ions, results in the three reactions shown in Equations 20, 21, and 22.

$$NH_4OH(aq) \rightleftharpoons NH_4^+(aq) + OH(aq) \rightleftharpoons NH_3(aq) + H_2O(l) \qquad \text{(Eq. 20)}$$

$$Bi^{3+}(aq) + 3\,NH_3(aq) + 3\,H_2O(l) \rightleftharpoons Bi(OH)_3(s, white) + 3\,NH_4^+(aq) \quad K = 3.3 \times 10^{39} \qquad \text{(Eq. 21)}$$

$$Cu^{2+}(aq) + 4\,NH_3(aq) \rightleftharpoons [Cu(NH_3)_4]^{2+}(aq, blue) \quad K = 3.8 \times 10^{12} \qquad \text{(Eq. 22)}$$

Although Cu^{2+} ion forms a soluble, bright blue ammonia complex in solutions of aqueous ammonia, Bi^{3+} ion does not form a stable ammonia complex. Instead, the very insoluble, white bismuth hydroxide, $Bi(OH)_3$, precipitates from this alkaline solution. Use of a base other than NH_3 would cause both cations to precipitate as hydroxides, instead of separating them.

If all Cd^{2+} ions were not removed in the previous step, the remaining dissolved Cd^{2+} ions will also form a soluble complex ion with ammonia, (tetrammine-cadmium(II) ion, $[Cd(NH_3)_4]^{2+}$), as shown in Equation 23.

$$Cd^{2+}(aq) + 4\,NH_3(aq) \rightleftharpoons [Cd(NH_3)_4]^{2+}(aq,\ colorless)\quad K = 1.0 \times 10^7 \qquad (Eq.\ 23)$$

Because $[Cd(NH_3)_4]^{2+}$ ion is colorless, it does not interfere with the tests for either Cu^{2+} or Bi^{3+} ion. If the solution does not have a high enough NH_3 concentration, Cd^{2+} ion may precipitate as cadmium(II) hydroxide, $Cd(OH)_2$, a white precipitate, which would be indistinguishable from the white $Bi(OH)_3$. If a white precipitate forms at this step in the procedure, the pH of the solution should be determined after thorough stirring. If the solution is strongly basic, the precipitate is $Bi(OH)_3$. The solution should be made strongly basic by adding aqueous NH_3. When the NH_3 concentration is high enough, all of the cadmium ion will form the ammine complex ion and remain dissolved.

When this mixture is centrifuged, the supernatant liquid will be blue if Cu^{2+} ion was originally present. This blue color results from the formation of tetramminecopper(II) ion, $[Cu(NH_3)_4]^{2+}$, by the reaction of Cu^{2+} ion with NH_3, as shown in Equation 22.

In this experiment, you will separate Bi^{3+}, Cu^{2+}, Cd^{2+}, and Sn^{4+} ions from a known solution and verify the presence of each cation by a confirmation test. Then, you will determine the cation present in an unknown solution containing one or more of the four cations, using the same procedure used with the known cation solution.

PROCEDURE

Some Notes on Semimicro Technique

1. *Precipitations:* The precipitating reagent should be added dropwise with stirring until precipitation is complete.

2. *Completeness of Precipitation:* So that interfering cations are not left in solution, it is often necessary, where noted, to allow the precipitate to settle in the test tube or to centrifuge the supernatant liquid and the precipitate, and then carefully add one additional drop of reagent. If more precipitate forms, a few more drops of reagent should be added and the above procedure repeated until no further precipitation is observed.

3. *Washing Precipitates:* To ensure removal of interfering ions from moist precipitates, it is necessary, where noted, to wash the precipitate. This procedure involves decanting the supernatant liquid, adding the required amount of a specified wash liquid to the tube containing the moist precipitate, mixing the precipitate and wash liquid thoroughly with a stirring rod, centrifuging, and decanting and discarding the wash liquid.

CAUTION

A solution in a small test tube cannot be heated safely over a direct flame.

---

4. *Heating a Solution:* Placing the test tube containing the solution to be heated in a hot or boiling water bath is generally a preferred method.

5. *Removing Supernatant Liquids:* Liquids over precipitates are most often removed by careful decantation. However, the supernatant liquid can carefully be withdrawn with a small medicine dropper, or pipet, if necessary.

Occasionally a precipitate does not centrifuge completely. To fully separate a supernatant liquid in such a situation, twist a small piece of cotton batting to a point and insert it partway into the tip of a clear eyedropper, leaving a tuft extending outside the tip. Draw up the supernatant liquid through the cotton, which will filter out the floating particles of precipitate. Enough precipitate should remain in the test tube for testing of those cations. Carefully remove the cotton and release the clear supernatant liquid into a clean 10×75-mm test tube.

I. Separating Selected Group II Cations

Figure 1 is a flowchart showing the separation and identification of the selected Group II cations Cu^{2+}, Cd^{2+}, Bi^{3+}, and Sn^{4+} ions.

CHEMICAL ALERT

6*M* ammonia—corrosive, toxic, and irritant
0.1*M* ammonium chloride—toxic and irritant
0.1*M* bismuth nitrate ion 0.3*M* HNO_3—toxic, irritant, and oxidant
0.1*M* cadmium chloride in 0.3*M* HNO_3—toxic and suspected carcinogen
0.1*M* copper(II) nitrate in 0.3*M* HNO_3—toxic, irritant, and oxidant
6*M* hydrochloric acid—toxic and corrosive
6*M* nitric acid—toxic, corrosive, and strong oxidant
3*M* potassium hydroxide—toxic and corrosive
1*M* thioacetamide—toxic and carcinogen
0.1*M* tin(IV) chloride in 0.3*M* HNO_3—corrosive and irritant

CAUTION

Wear departmentally approved eye protection while doing this experiment.

II. Precipitating, Separating, and Confirming Selected Group II Cations

A. Precipitating Group II Sulfides

Obtain from your laboratory instructor, in an appropriate container, a known mixture containing the selected Group II cations. With a clean dropper, transfer 15 drops of the known solution to a clean 10×75-mm test tube. Estimate the pH of this solution, using short-range pH test paper. The solution should have a pH of 0.5 ± 0.3, indicating a H_3O^+ ion concentration of approximately 0.35*M*. If the pH of the solution is not within the specified pH range, adjust the pH as follows.

CAUTION

6*M* hydrochloric acid is a corrosive, toxic solution that can cause burns. Prevent contact with your eyes, skin, and clothing. Avoid inhaling vapors and ingesting the solution.

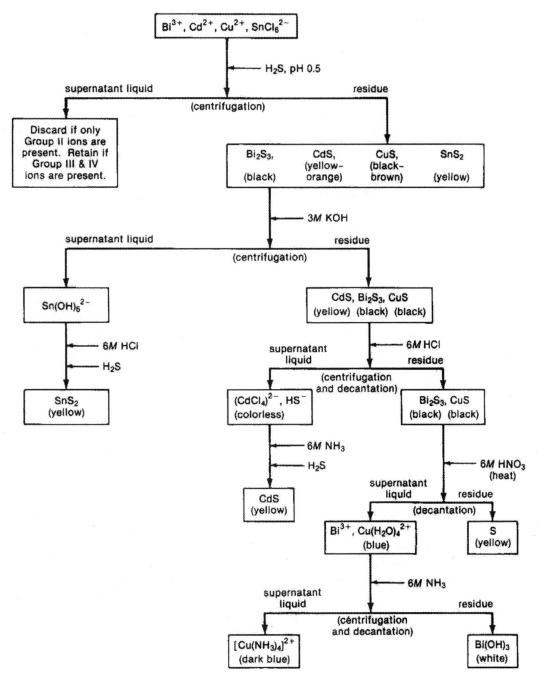

Figure 1
Flowchart for separating Group II ions

> **CAUTION**
>
> **6M ammonia is a corrosive, toxic solution. Prevent contact with your eyes, skin, and clothing. Avoid inhaling vapors and ingesting the solution.**

Prepare 0.5M solutions of HCl or NH$_3$ as required, by diluting 1 drop of a 6M solution with 11 drops of distilled water and mixing the solutions thoroughly with a clean glass stirring rod. Add the required $0.5M$ solution dropwise with stirring to the solution until the pH is within the indicated range.

It is important that the pH of the solution be within the specified pH range. If the pH is greater than 0.8, that is, if the H_3O^+ ion concentration is less than $0.2M$, ions other than Group II ions may precipitate. If the pH is less than 0.2, that is, if the H_3O^+ ion concentration is greater than $0.6M$, the sulfide ion concentration may be too low to effect a complete precipitation of the Group II sulfides.

CAUTION   ⚠️

Thioacetamide has proven to be a carcinogen in animal feeding studies. It is safe to use when handled prudently. Avoid skin contact with the thioacetamide solution. Wash your hands thoroughly with soap or detergent after using the solution.

Using a clean dropper, add 10 drops of $1M$ thioacetamide solution to the acidic solution. Stir the mixture with a clean glass stirring rod. Place the test tube and its contents in a boiling water bath for 10 min. While the reaction mixture is heating, prepare a dilute solution of aqueous NH_3 by adding 3 drops of $6M$ NH_3 to 2 mL of distilled water. Retain this dilute NH_3 solution for later use. If $0.5M$ NH_3 was prepared previously, it may be used instead of preparing this NH_3 solution.

Remove the tube containing the reaction mixture from the boiling water bath. Cool the tube and its contents by running tap water over the outside of the tube. The cooling of the mixture aids the precipitation of CdS. Add 1 drop of the dilute NH_3 solution prepared previously. The addition of dilute NH_3 promotes the precipitation of CdS and SnS_2, both of which have a tendency to form supersaturated solutions. Thoroughly stir the mixture with a glass stirring rod. Centrifuge the tube and its contents for 2 min.

Without separating the supernatant liquid from the precipitate, add 5 additional drops of $1M$ thioacetamide to the mixture. Place the tube and its contents in a boiling water bath for 2 additional min. Cool the tube containing the mixture by running tap water over the outside of the tube. Add 1 drop of the prepared dilute NH_3 solution from a clean dropper. Stir the mixture with a clean glass stirring rod. Centrifuge the test tube and its contents for 2 min. Remove the supernatant liquid by decanting it from the precipitate.

NOTE: In all parts of this experiment, follow the directions of your laboratory instructor for discarding reaction mixtures and unused reagents.

If only Group II cations were present in the original sample solution, discard the supernatant liquid. If the sample solution is to be analyzed for Group III and/or IV cations, retain and label the supernatant liquid.

Wash the precipitate remaining in the test tube by adding 1 mL of $0.1M$ ammonium chloride (NH_4Cl) solution to the precipitate. Stir the mixture well with a clean glass stirring rod. The electrolyte, NH_4Cl, helps to keep the sulfides from forming a colloidal suspension. Centrifuge the tube and its contents for 2 min. Decant the supernatant liquid from the precipitate.

Discard the supernatant liquid. Retain the precipitate for use in the next section.

Record all observations on Data Sheet 1.

B. Separating and Confirming Tin(IV)

CAUTION ⚠

3M potassium hydroxide solution (KOH) is a corrosive, toxic solution that can cause burns. Prevent contact with your eyes, skin, and clothing. Avoid ingesting the solution.

Use a clean dropper to add 20 drops of 3M KOH to the Group II sulfide precipitate in the test tube. Use a clean dropper to add 1 drop of 1M thioacetamide solution to the mixture. The thioacetamide ensures that the sulfide ion concentration will be sufficient to prevent the CuS from dissolving. Thoroughly stir the mixture with a clean glass stirring rod to ensure the complete suspension of the precipitate. Loosely stopper the tube and carefully heat the tube and its contents in a boiling water bath for 2 min. Do not heat longer than 2 min, because CuS might dissolve in the hot basic solution.

Immediately centrifuge the test tube and its contents for 2 min. Decant the supernatant liquid containing the $[Sn(OH)_6]^{2-}$ ions from the precipitate into a 15 × 125-mm test tube.

Wash the remaining precipitate by using 10 drops of distilled water. Thoroughly stir the mixture with a clean glass stirring rod. Centrifuge the tube containing the mixture for 2 min. Decant the supernatant liquid from the precipitate. Discard the supernatant liquid.

Follow the same procedure to wash the precipitate a second time. Discard the supernatant liquid. Retain and label the tube containing the precipitate for use in Part C.

Use a clean dropper to add 6M HCl dropwise to the supernatant liquid containing the $[Sn(OH)_6]^{2-}$ ions in the 15 × 125-mm test tube until the solution tests acidic to litmus paper. Use a clean dropper to add 5 drops of 1M thioacetamide to this solution. Heat the test tube and its contents in a boiling water bath for 2 min.

Record all observations on Data Sheet 1.

C. Separating and Confirming Cadmium(II)

Use a clean dropper to add 10 drops of distilled water to the sulfide precipitate retained from Part B. Then, add 2 drops of 6M HCl from a clean dropper. Stir thoroughly with a clean glass stirring rod. Heat the test tube and its contents 2 min in a hot water bath.

Centrifuge the tube and its contents for 2 min. Carefully decant the supernatant liquid from the precipitate into a clean 15 × 125-mm test tube. If some of the precipitate is transferred with the supernatant liquid, remove it. The eyedropper and cotton wadding technique described previously may be used to remove the precipitate.

Wash the precipitate with 10 drops of distilled water, label the tube, and retain for use in Part D.

Add 6M NH$_3$ to the clear supernatant liquid until it is basic to litmus paper. If no precipitate appears, add 2 drops of 1M thioacetamide, and heat the test tube and its contents for 2 min in a hot water bath. Record all observations on Data Sheet 1.

D. Separating and Confirming Bismuth(III) and Copper(II)

CAUTION

6M nitric acid is a corrosive, toxic solution that can cause severe burns and discolor your skin. Prevent contact with your eyes, skin, clothing, and combustible materials. Avoid inhaling vapors and ingesting the solution.

To the sulfide precipitate retained from the previous section, add 10 drops of 6M nitric acid (HNO_3) from a clean dropper while stirring the mixture with a clean glass stirring rod. Heat the tube and its contents in a boiling water bath for 5 min. If there is any undissolved residue in the tube, decant the supernatant liquid from this residue.

Add sufficient 6M NH_3 from a clean dropper to make the solution just alkaline to litmus paper. Add 10 additional drops of 6M NH_3. Thoroughly stir the solution using a clean glass stirring rod, and allow the solution to cool. Use indicator paper to check the pH of the solution after thoroughly mixing it. If the solution is not strongly basic, add 6M NH_3 until it is. If insufficient NH_3 is added, Cu^{2+} ion may precipitate as $Cu(OH)_2$ with the $Bi(OH)_3$ instead of forming $[Cu(NH_3)_4]^{2+}$ ion and remaining in the supernatant liquid.

Centrifuge the tube containing the mixture for 2 min. Decant the supernatant liquid from the precipitate into a clean centrifuge tube.

Wash the precipitate with 10 drops of 6M NH_3 from a clean dropper. Centrifuge the tube and its contents for 2 min. Decant the supernatant liquid from the precipitate, and discard the supernatant liquid.

Record all observations on Data Sheet 1.

III. Analyzing a Group II Unknown Cation Solution

Obtain a solution containing one or more of the Group II cations from your laboratory instructor. Record the unknown identification number on Data Sheet 2.

Repeat the procedure in Part II with this solution. List on Data Sheet 2 the cations you found in your unknown solution. List evidence on your Data Sheet to prove the presence of the cations reported.

If the unknown solution is part of a general unknown that originally contained ions from Group I, follow the same procedure as in Section II, using 15 drops of the supernatant liquid from the initial precipitation of the Group I cations.

CAUTION

Wash your hands thoroughly with soap or detergent before leaving the laboratory.

_____   _____   _____
Name   *Section*   *Date*

Post-Laboratory Questions

(Use the spaces provided for the answers and additional paper if necessary.)

   1. A solution is known to contain Bi^{3+} ion or Cd^{2+} ion or both. Describe the test(s) that could be used to separate and identify these ions. Describe the results you would expect to see for each ion, if that ion were present.

   2. (1) Describe how adding a solution of KOH to the original sulfide precipitate results in the separation of Sn^{4+} ion from the other Group II cations.

   (2) Why wouldn't a weak base, such as aqueous NH_3, work just as well as aqueous KOH in (1)?

3. How does the addition of aqueous NH_3 to a solution separate and identify Cu^{2+} and Bi^{3+} ions? Why wouldn't the addition of a strong base, such as KOH, work just as well as the addition of aqueous NH_3?

4. Why does CdS dissolve in HCl, when CuS and Bi_2S_3 will not?

Name   Section   Date

Data Sheet 1

(Record below all observations made while performing Part II of this experiment.)

II. Precipitating, Separating, and Confirming Selected Group II Cations

A. Precipitating Group II sulfides

B. Separating and confirming tin(IV)

C. Separating and confirming cadmium(II)

D. Separating and confirming bismuth(III) and copper(II)

Data Sheet 2

III. Analyzing a Group II Unknown Cation Solution

unknown identification number _____

cations found _____

_____

_____

Present evidence to prove the presence of the cations listed.

Name   Section   Date

Pre-Laboratory Assignment

1. Read an authoritative source for a discussion of the techniques to be used in this experiment.

2. Consult a reference book regarding the hazards associated with H_2S. On the basis of this information, explain the merits of generating H_2S in the solution in which it is to be used. Briefly explain the chemistry involved in this generation.

3. Write equations for the following chemical reactions. State the color of the products for each reaction.

   (1) $Cd^{2+}(aq) + S^{2-}(aq)$

   (2) $SnS_2(s) + OH^-(aq)$

   (3) $Cu^{2+}(aq) + NH_3(aq)$

4. For a solution containing at least one of the cations involved in this experiment, answer the following questions.

   (1) A solution is acidified to pH 0.5, and H_2S is added. A dark precipitate results. Which cation(s) may be present?

   (2) KOH is added to the precipitate from (1). The supernatant liquid is separated from the dark precipitate and tested with HCl/H_2S. A colorless solution results, with no precipitate. Which cation(s) may be present?

   (3) The remaining precipitate from (1) is treated with dilute HCl. The supernatant liquid is tested with NH_3 and H_2S. A yellow precipitate results. Which cation(s) may be present?

   (4) The precipitate left from the first step in (3) is dissolved in HNO_3, and the resulting supernatant liquid is treated with NH_3. A blue supernatant liquid results, with no precipitate. Give the identity of all Group II cations present in the original solution.

5. Describe how to check a solution for completeness of precipitation.

The Chemistry and Qualitative Analysis of Cations: Groups III and IV

Prepared by James G. Boyles, Bates College, and
Judith C. Foster and David S. Page, Bowdoin College

PURPOSE OF THE EXPERIMENT

Develop the chemistry of selected Group III and IV cations (Fe^{3+}/Fe^{2+}, Ni^{2+}, Cr^{3+}, Ba^{2+}, and Ca^{2+} ions). Use this chemistry to establish a procedure for verifying qualitatively the presence of these selected cations.

BACKGROUND INFORMATION

A selected group of chemically important and commonly encountered cations appear in Table 1 on the next page.

Of these cations, the Group I cations, Ag^+, Hg_2^{2+}, and Pb^{2+} ions, may be removed from solution by precipitation as chlorides. The Group II cations, Bi^{3+}, Cu^{2+}, Cd^{2+}, and Sn^{4+} ions, form insoluble sulfide precipitates even at very low sulfide ion (S^{2-}) concentrations. The Group III cations are Ni^{2+}, Cr^{3+}, and Fe^{2+} ions. Although some Group III sulfides are very insoluble, they are considerably more soluble than the Group II sulfides. By controlling the S^{2-} ion concentration at a low enough level, we can first precipitate just the Group II sulfides. Sulfide ion concentration can be adjusted by changing pH, because hydrogen sulfide (H_2S) is an acid, as shown in Equation 1.

$$H_2S(aq) + 2\,H_2O(l) \rightleftharpoons 2\,H_3O^+(aq) + S^{2-}(aq) \qquad \text{(Eq. 1)}$$

At low pH, the S^{2-} ion will be present primarily as H_2S or HS^- ion. Although the S^{2-} ion concentration is exceedingly low, it is high enough to precipitate the Group II cations. After the Group II cations are removed as sulfides, the Group III cations may then be precipitated as sulfides by raising the pH of the solution and generating more H_2S. Adding hydroxide ion (OH^-) to the solution shifts the equilibrium shown in Equation 1 by lowering the H_3O^+ ion concentration. The resulting higher S^{2-} ion concentration is sufficient to precipitate the Group III sulfides. Some, but not all, of the Group III cations initially form a hydroxide precipitate in this basic solution. The hydroxides of all but Cr^{3+} ion are converted to sulfides

Table 1 *Nomenclature and formulas of some cations*

cation	common name	formula
barium		Ba^{2+}
bismuth(III)		Bi^{3+}
calcium		Ca^{2+}
cadmium(II)		Cd^{2+}
chromium(III)	chromic	Cr^{3+}
copper(II)	cupric	Cu^{2+}
iron(III)	ferric	Fe^{3+}
lead(II)	plumbous	Pb^{2+}
mercury(I)	mercurous	Hg_2^{2+}
nickel(II)	nickelous	Ni^{2+}
silver(I)		Ag^+
tin(IV)	stannic	Sn^{4+}

in the presence of S^{2-} ion in the solution. Cr^{3+} ion remains as insoluble chromium(III) hydroxide, $Cr(OH)_3$, and, therefore, is separated with the other Group III cations.

The Group III cations can be separated from the Group IV cations by treating a basic solution of the cations with H_2S to precipitate iron(II) sulfide (FeS, ferrous sulfide) and nickel(II) sulfide (NiS, nickelous sulfide). Although chromium(III) sulfide (Cr_2S_3) does not form, Cr^{3+} ion precipitates as $Cr(OH)_3$ in mildly basic solution and is thus classified as a Group III cation. The Group IV cations, Ba^{2+} and Ca^{2+}, remain in solution. After the cations are separated, we can make use of the different chemical properties of each cation to effect a positive qualitative verification of its presence.

I. Separating Group III Cations from Group IV Cations

The Group III ions, Fe^{2+}, Ni^{2+}, and Cr^{3+}, may be separated from the Group IV ions, Ba^{2+} and Ca^{2+}, by taking advantage of the large differences in the solubility product constants of the hydroxides and sulfides of the cations of these groups. The OH^- ion concentration of a solution containing Group III and IV ions may be maintained at a concentration of approximately $1.0 \times 10^{-5}M$ by use of a buffer that is an aqueous solution of ammonia (NH_3) to which an equimolar amount of an ammonium salt has been added. A solution is buffered if it resists changes in pH when small amounts of H_3O^+ ion or of OH^- ion are added. Ammonia reacts with water according to the equilibrium shown in Equation 2.

$$NH_3(aq) + H_2O(l) \rightleftharpoons NH_4^+(aq) + OH^-(aq) \qquad K_b = 1.8 \times 10^{-5} \qquad \text{(Eq. 2)}$$

Because the equilibrium constant for the reaction is small, the amount of NH_4^+ ion in solution is, ordinarily, small. In order to establish a buffer, an equimolar amount of an ammonium salt, such as ammonium chloride (NH_4Cl), is added to an aqueous solution of ammonia. The pH of such a solution is very close to 9. Further addition or removal of OH^- ion results in small changes in the relative concentrations of NH_3 and NH_4^+ ion but not in the concentration of OH^- ion. That is, the system resists any large change in pH.

Table 2 *Solubility constants at 25 °C*

ion	sulfide	hydroxide	minimum [OH⁻] to precipitate 0.1M cation†	pH at which 0.1M cation will precipitate†
Group III				
Fe^{2+}	4.9×10^{-18}	2.0×10^{-15}	1.4×10^{-7}	6.9
Fe^{3+}	$1 \times 10^{-88*}$	6.0×10^{-38}	2.2×10^{-10}	9.7
Ni^{2+}	1.8×10^{-21}	2.0×10^{-16}	4.5×10^{-8}	6.7
Cr^{3+}	not stable in H_2O	7.0×10^{-31}	9.1×10^{-11}	4.0
Group IV				
Ba^{2+}	not stable in H_2O	5.0×10^{-3}	2.2×10^{-1}	13.3
Ca^{2+}	not stable in H_2O	7.9×10^{-6}	8.9×10^{-2}	12.9

† Precipitated as the hydroxide.
* Fe_2S_3 in acid decomposes to FeS and S.

Looking at the data in Table 2, we can conclude that all of the hydroxides are reasonably insoluble, but that the Group IV hydroxides are much more soluble than those of Group III.

In a buffered solution such as that described, the OH⁻ ion concentration is at a level sufficient to qualitatively precipitate the Group III hydroxides but not the more soluble Group IV hydroxides. By examining the data in Table 2, we can see that this statement is accurate. The data show the pH at which hydroxide precipitates will form when OH⁻ ion is added to the cations with a concentration of 0.1M. The most soluble of the Group III hydroxides is iron(II) hydroxide, [Fe(OH)₂, ferrous hydroxide]. The relative solubilities of these hydroxides can be determined by comparing the OH⁻ ion concentration necessary to precipitate each cation, as listed in Table 2.

The Fe^{2+} ion concentration in a solution buffered at an OH⁻ ion concentration of $1.0 \times 10^{-5}M$ can be calculated from the solubility product of Fe(OH)₂, as follows:

$$K_{sp} = [Fe^{2+}][OH^-]^2 = 2.0 \times 10^{-15} \qquad \text{(Eq. 3)}$$

$$[Fe^{2+}] = \frac{2.0 \times 10^{-15}}{1.0 \times 10^{-10}} = 2 \times 10^{-5} \qquad \text{(Eq. 4)}$$

If the initial concentration of Fe^{2+} ion is assumed to be 0.10M, the precipitation of Fe^{2+} ion as the hydroxide is more than 99.9% complete.

The concentration of Ca^{2+} ion that can exist in a solution with a OH⁻ ion concentration of $1.0 \times 10^{-5}M$ can be calculated from the solubility product constant given in Table 2.

$$K_{sp} = [Ca^{2+}][OH^-]^2 = 7.9 \times 10^{-6} \qquad \text{(Eq. 5)}$$

$$[Ca^{2+}] = \frac{7.9 \times 10^{-6}}{1.0 \times 10^{-10}} = 7.9 \times 10^4 \qquad \text{(Eq. 6)}$$

The Ca^{2+} ion concentration that can exist in a $1.0 \times 10^{-5}M$ hydroxide solution is quite large, so that essentially no precipitation of Ca^{2+} ion occurs from such a solution. Because barium hydroxide, $Ba(OH)_2$, is even more soluble, neither Group IV cation will precipitate under these conditions.

Thus, from the solubility product constants we can show that a separation of Group III and IV ions by precipitation with OH^- ion is feasible. In actuality, nickel(II) hydroxide [$Ni(OH)_2$, nickelous hydroxide] does not precipitate from solutions containing NH_3, even though the OH^- ion concentration is sufficiently large. In the presence of NH_3, Ni^{2+} ion forms a stable water-soluble ammonia complex, hexammine-nickel(II), $[Ni(NH_3)_6]^{2+}$, as shown in Equation 7.

$$Ni^{2+}(aq) + 6\,NH_3(aq) \rightleftharpoons [Ni(NH_3)_6]^{2+}(aq, \text{blue to lavender}) \qquad K = 2.0 \times 10^8 \qquad \text{(Eq. 7)}$$

The other Group III cations present do not form stable ammonia complexes. In a solution buffered with NH_3/NH_4^+ ion, the system will contain

precipitate	solution
$Fe(OH)_2$	$[Ni(NH_3)_6]^{2+}$
$Cr(OH)_3$	Ba^{2+}
	Ca^{2+}

At this point in the process, the Group III $[Ni(NH_3)_6]^{2+}$ complex ion is still in solution with the Group IV cations. If thioacetamide (CH_3CSNH_2) is added to this basic solution and the solution is heated, the equilibrium in the reaction shown in Equation 8 is shifted to the right, because the forward reaction is endothermic. Hence, HS^- ion will be generated in the solution.

$$\underset{\substack{\|\\ S}}{H_3C-C-NH_2}(aq) + 2\,OH^-(aq) \rightleftharpoons \underset{\substack{\|\\ O}}{CH_3-C-O^-}(aq) + NH_3(aq) + HS^-(aq) \qquad \text{(Eq. 8)}$$

In basic solution, the dissociation of HS^- ion, as shown in the equilibria in Equations 9 and 10, is nearly complete. The OH^- ion reacts with the H_3O^+ ion produced in Equation 9 to form water, as shown in Equation 10. To replenish the H_3O^+ ion in the equilibria shown in Equation 9, more HS^- ion dissociates. If sufficient OH^- ion is present, the dissociation reaction proceeds to completion.

$$HS^-(aq) + H_2O(l) \rightleftharpoons S^{2-}(aq) + H_3O^+(aq) \qquad \text{(Eq. 9)}$$

$$H_3O^+(aq) + OH^-(aq) \rightleftharpoons 2\,H_2O(l) \qquad \text{(Eq. 10)}$$

Under these conditions, NiS and FeS are formed, as the reactions in Equations 11 and 12 indicate.

$$[Ni(NH_3)_6]^{2+}(aq) + S^{2-}(aq) \rightleftharpoons NiS(s, \text{black}) + 6\,NH_3(aq) \qquad K = 2.0 \times 10^{12} \qquad \text{(Eq. 11)}$$

$$Fe(OH)_2(s) + S^{2-}(aq) \rightleftharpoons FeS(s, \text{balck}) + 2\,OH^-(aq) \qquad K = 4.0 \times 10^2 \qquad \text{(Eq. 12)}$$

Table 3 *Characteristic colors of some Group III and IV ions and compounds*

aqueous ion	hydroxide	sulfide
$[Fe(H_2O)_6]^{2+}$ (pale green)	$Fe(OH)_2$ (green)	FeS (black)
$[Fe(H_2O)_6]^{3+}$ (reddish-brown)	$Fe(OH)_3$ (rusty)	Fe_2S_3 (yellow-green)
$[FeCl_4]^-$ (yellow, in HCl soln)		
$[Cr(H_2O)_6]^{3+}$ (blue)	$Cr(OH)_3$ (gray-green)	
CrO_4^{2-} (yellow)	CrO_5 (peroxide, blue)	
$[Ni(H_2O)_6]^{2+}$ (green)	$Ni(OH)_2$ (green)	NiS (black)
$[Ni(NH_3)_6]^{2+}$ (blue to lavender)		
Ba^{2+} (colorless)	$Ba(OH)_2$ (white)	
Ca^{2+} (colorless)	$Ca(OH)_2$ (white)	

Because Cr^{3+} ion does not form a stable sulfide from an aqueous solution, $Cr(OH)_3$ will remain in the precipitate. The supernatant liquid containing Group IV cations Ba^{2+} and Ca^{2+} ions can now be removed from the Group III precipitates of NiS, FeS, and $Cr(OH)_3$ by centrifugation and decantation.

Careful observation of the colors of the precipitates formed when the solution is first made basic, and later when S^{2-} ion is added, may give good clues to the presence or absence of certain cations. However, dark-colored precipitates often mask light-colored ones, and mixtures of indeterminate color often result. Table 3 gives characteristic colors of some ions and precipitates that are relevant to Group III and Group IV analysis but are not involved in final confirmation reactions.

Care must be exercised to avoid making the Group III and IV cation solution too alkaline. Adding *excess* strong base to a precipitate of $Cr(OH)_3$ forms the soluble chromite complex ion, tetrahydroxodiaquochromate(III), $[Cr(OH)_4(H_2O)_2]^-$, which is more conveniently represented as $[Cr(OH)_4]^-$ ion.

This is a significant problem only at pH 13, which can be avoided experimentally by buffering the basic solution at pH 9.

II. Separating and Confirming Group III Cations

A. Precipitating Group III Cations

Chromium(III) hydroxide readily dissolves in acidic solution, as shown in Equations 13 and 14.

$$Cr(OH)_3(s) \rightleftharpoons Cr^{3+}(aq) + 3\,OH^-(aq) \qquad \text{(Eq. 13)}$$

$$3\,OH^-(aq) + 3\,H_3O^+(aq) \rightleftharpoons 6\,H_2O(l) \qquad \text{(Eq. 14)}$$

Addition of H_3O^+ ion to this system shifts both of these equilibria to the right, dissolving the solid $Cr(OH)_3$, and resulting in free Cr^{3+} ion in solution.

Iron(II) sulfide dissolves in acidic solution, as shown in Equations 15 and 16.

$$FeS(s) \rightleftharpoons Fe^{2+}(aq) + S^{2-}(aq) \qquad \text{(Eq. 15)}$$

$$S^{2-}(aq) + 2\,H_3O^+(aq) \rightleftharpoons H_2S(aq) + 2\,H_2O(l) \qquad \text{(Eq. 16)}$$

If the unknown was not analyzed for Group II cations, iron may be present as Fe^{3+} ion. In such a case, Fe^{3+} ion would precipitate as iron(III) hydroxide [$Fe(OH)_3$, ferric hydroxide] and then as iron(III) sulfide (Fe_2S_3, ferric sulfide) with the other Group III sulfides. Any Fe_2S_3 present would dissolve in acidic solution, and additionally, the Fe^{3+} ion would be reduced to Fe^{2+} ion, as shown in Equations 17 and 18.

$$Fe_2S_3(s) \rightleftharpoons 2\,Fe^{3+}(aq) + 3\,S^{2-}(aq) \qquad \text{(Eq. 17)}$$

$$2\,Fe^{3+}(aq) + 2\,S^{2-}(aq) + 2\,H_3O^+(aq) \rightleftharpoons 2\,Fe^{2+}(aq) + H_2S(aq) + S(s) + 2\,H_2O(l) \qquad \text{(Eq. 18)}$$

Addition of H_3O^+ ion shifts the equilibrium in Equations 17 and 18 to the right, thus dissolving the solid iron sulfides and resulting in Fe^{2+} ion in solution.

Nickel(II) sulfide has such a small K_{sp} that it does not dissolve appreciably in acidic solution, unless an oxidizing agent such as nitrate ion (NO_3^-) is present. Thus, if HCl is added to the combined FeS, Fe_2S_3, $Cr(OH)_3$, and NiS precipitates, the iron and chromium will go into solution as Fe^{2+} and Cr^{3+} ions, leaving solid NiS undissolved.

B. Separating and Confirming Chromium(III)

When the strong oxidizing agent hydrogen peroxide (H_2O_2) is added to an alkaline solution of Fe^{2+} and Cr^{3+} ions, the Cr^{3+} ion is oxidized to chromate ion (CrO_4^{2-}) while the Fe^{2+} ion is oxidized to Fe^{3+} ion, which precipitates as $Fe(OH)_3$. These reactions are shown in Equations 19, 20, and 21.

$$2\,Cr^{3+}(aq) + 3\,H_2O_2(aq) + 10\,OH^-(aq) \rightleftharpoons 2\,CrO_4^{2-}(aq) + 8\,H_2O(l) \qquad \text{(Eq. 19)}$$

$$2\,Fe^{2+}(aq) + H_2O_2(aq) \rightleftharpoons 2\,Fe^{3+}(aq) + 2\,OH^-(aq) \qquad \text{(Eq. 20)}$$

$$Fe^{3+}(aq) + 3\,OH^-(aq) \rightleftharpoons Fe(OH)_3(s) \qquad \text{(Eq. 21)}$$

Care must be taken to keep the solution sufficiently basic. Otherwise the reactions represented by Equations 19, 20, and 21 might not occur, rendering further analysis pointless. After the reactions have occurred, the solution should have a pH between 9 and 10.

Chromate ion is yellow in basic aqueous solution. After separation from the rusty solid $Fe(OH)_3$, the presence of CrO_4^{2-} ion can be confirmed by the following reactions. Nitric acid is added to make the solution acidic. Hydrogen peroxide is added. In *acidic* solution, H_2O_2 is a reducing agent, as shown in the half-reaction in Equation 22.

$$H_2O_2(aq) + 2\,H_2O(l) \rightleftharpoons O_2(aq) + 2\,H_3O^+(aq) + 2\,e^- \qquad \text{(Eq. 22)}$$

In acidic H_2O_2 solution, CrO_4^{2-} ion is reduced to Cr^{3+} ion via a two-step process, as shown in Equations 23, 24, and 25.

$$2\,CrO_4^{2-}(aq) + 2\,H_3O^+(aq) \rightleftharpoons Cr_2O_7^{2-}(aq) + 3\,H_2O(l) \qquad \text{(Eq. 23)}$$

$$Cr_2O_7{}^{2-}(aq) + 4\,H_2O_2(aq) + 2\,H_3O^+(aq) \rightleftharpoons 2\,CrO_5(aq) + 7\,H_2O(l) \qquad \text{(Eq. 24)}$$

$$4\,CrO_5(aq) + 12\,H_3O^+(aq) \rightleftharpoons 4\,Cr^{3+}(aq) + 7\,O_2(g) + 18\,H_2O(l) \qquad \text{(Eq. 25)}$$

In acidic solution, $CrO_4{}^{2-}$ ion is converted to dichromate ion ($Cr_2O_7{}^{2-}$). When H_2O_2 is added, the $Cr_2O_7{}^{2-}$ ion reacts to form in solution dark blue chromium(VI) peroxide (CrO_5), in which one oxygen has a -2 oxidation state and the other four have a -1 oxidation state. In solution, CrO_5 is unstable and rapidly decomposes to Cr^{3+} ion, which has a much less intense blue color, with evolution of molecular oxygen. After destroying any remaining H_2O_2, the Cr^{3+} ion is precipitated by the addition of $6M$ sodium hydroxide (NaOH) solution (reversing Equation 13).

C. Confirming Iron(III)

The $Fe(OH)_3$ precipitate is dissolved by addition of acid, as shown in Equations 26 and 27.

$$Fe(OH)_3(s) \rightleftharpoons Fe^{3+}(aq) + 3\,OH^-(aq) \qquad \text{(Eq. 26)}$$

$$OH^-(aq) + H_3O^+(aq) \rightleftharpoons 2\,H_2O(l) \qquad \text{(Eq. 27)}$$

Thiocyanate ion (SCN^-) is then added, and the formation of the soluble deep-red thiocyanatoiron(III) complex, $[FeSCN]^{2+}$, as shown in Equation 28, confirms the presence of iron.

$$Fe^{3+}(aq) + SCN^-(aq) \rightleftharpoons [FeSCN]^{2+}(aq,\ \text{deep red}) \qquad K = 1.0 \times 10^2 \qquad \text{(Eq. 28)}$$

D. Confirming Nickel(II)

The precipitate remaining after Cr^{3+} and Fe^{2+}/Fe^{3+} ions have been removed is NiS. Because NiS is not readily soluble in HCl, aqua regia (a mixture of HCl and HNO_3) must be used to dissolve the NiS. Upon addition of aqua regia, followed by heating, several redox and complex-ion equilibria are established, as shown in Equations 29, 30, and 31.

$$NiS(s) \rightleftharpoons Ni^{2+}(aq) + S^{2-}(aq) \qquad \text{(Eq. 29)}$$

$$Ni^{2+}(aq) + 4\,Cl^-(aq) \rightleftharpoons [NiCl_4]^{2-}(aq,\ \text{green}) \qquad \text{(Eq. 30)}$$

$$3\,S^{2-}(aq) + 2\,NO_3{}^-(aq) + 8\,H_3O^+(aq) \rightleftharpoons 3\,S(s) + 2\,NO(aq) + 12\,H_2O(l) \qquad \text{(Eq. 31)}$$

Nitrogen(II) oxide (NO, nitric monoxide or nitric oxide), a product from the reaction in Equation 31, evolves rapidly from the warm solution as gaseous NO, as shown in Equation 32. Oxygen gas in the air reacts rapidly with gaseous NO to form the reddish-brown gas, nitrogen(IV) oxide (NO_2, nitrogen dioxide), as shown in Equation 33.

$$NO(aq) \rightleftharpoons NO(g) \qquad \text{(Eq. 32)}$$

$$2\,NO(g) + O_2(g) \rightleftharpoons 2\,NO_2(g) \qquad \text{(Eq. 33)}$$

Nickel(II) ion is produced according to the equilibrium in Equation 29. If chloride ion (Cl^-) is present, Ni^{2+} ion will complex with the Cl^- ion, as shown in Equation 30. The equilibrium constant for Equation 30 is large, favoring the formation of tetrachloronickelate(II) ion, $[NiCl_4]^{2-}$. Additional NiS will dissolve in an attempt to maintain the Ni^{2+} ion required for the equilibrium in Equation 29. At the same time, the S^{2-} ion present from the dissociation of NiS in Equation 29 is oxidized by acidic NO_3^- ion and is precipitated as solid S, as shown in Equation 31. In addition, NO is liberated as a gas. Because the equilibrium associated with the reaction shown in Equation 31 is shifted toward product formation, the precipitation of solid S and the evolution of NO gas, additional NiS will dissolve in an attempt to maintain the S^{2-} ion concentration required for the equilibrium in Equation 29.

The high Cl^-, NO_3^-, and H_3O^+ ion concentrations, combined with the loss of NO from the warm solution as NO(g), are sufficient to shift these equilibria to the right, thus dissolving NiS. The resulting $[NiCl_4]^{2-}$ complex can be converted to the hexamminenickel(II) complex, $[Ni(NH_3)_6]^{2+}$, by addition of aqueous NH_3, as shown in Equation 34.

$$[NiCl_4]^{2-}(aq) + 6\,NH_3(aq) \rightleftharpoons [Ni(NH_3)_6]^{2+}(aq, \text{ blue to lavender}) + 4\,Cl^-(aq) \qquad \text{(Eq. 34)}$$

Dimethylglyoxime, $(CH_3)_2C_2(NOH)_2$, is an organic compound that forms a strongly bonded complex with nickel in basic solution. The dimethylglyoxime (DMG) is partially deprotonated in basic solution allowing it to form a complex whose structure is shown in Figure 1. The size and electronic structure of the Ni^{2+} ion is well suited for the formation of this complex. When a small amount of dimethylglyoxime is added to the solution containing $[Ni(NH_3)_6]^{2+}$ ion, a red precipitate forms, as shown in Equation 35. This reaction confirms the presence of nickel.

$$2(CH_3)_2C_2(NOH)_2(aq) + [Ni(NH_3)_6]^{2+}(aq) \rightleftharpoons$$
$$2\,NH_4^+(aq) + 4\,NH_3(aq) + NiC_8H_{14}N_4O_4(s, \text{ red}) \qquad \text{(Eq. 35)}$$

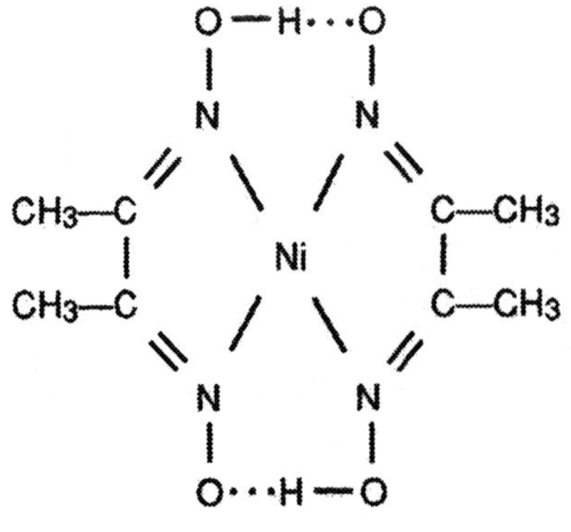

Figure 1
The structure of the nickel(II)–DMG complex

III. Separating and Confirming Group IV Cations

A. Precipitating Group IV Cations

After thioacetamide is added, the supernatant liquid will contain the Group IV cations Ba^{2+} and Ca^{2+}. Both of these ions can be precipitated as white carbonates by adding carbonate ion (CO_3^{2-}), as shown in Equations 36 and 37.

$$Ba^{2+}(aq) + CO_3^{2-}(aq) \rightleftharpoons BaCO_3(s, \text{white}) \qquad K_{sp} = 5.0 \times 10^{-9} \qquad \text{(Eq. 36)}$$

$$Ca^{2+}(aq) + CO_3^{2-}(aq) \rightleftharpoons CaCO_3(s, \text{white}) \qquad K_{sp} = 7.5 \times 10^{-9} \qquad \text{(Eq. 37)}$$

B. Separating and Confirming Barium

Like all carbonates, barium carbonate ($BaCO_3$) and calcium carbonate ($CaCO_3$) are soluble in acidic solution. Hydronium ion reacts with CO_3^{2-} ion and shifts the equilibria in the reactions shown in Equations 38 and 39 to the right, leading to the evolution of carbon(IV) oxide gas (CO_2, carbon dioxide).

In this experiment, acetic acid (CH_3COOH) is used to dissolve the carbonate precipitate. In the process, the acid is converted to the acetate anion (CH_3COO^-), as shown in Equation 39.

$$BaCO_3(s) \rightleftharpoons Ba^{2+}(aq) + CO_3^{2-}(aq) \qquad \text{(Eq. 38)}$$

$$CO_3^{2-}(aq) + 2\,CH_3COOH(aq) \rightleftharpoons CO_2(g) + 2\,CH_3COO^-(aq) + 2\,H_2O(l) \qquad \text{(Eq. 39)}$$

Acetate ion is present in solution after all the solid carbonates dissolve. If, after all the carbonates just dissolve, an additional amount of acetic acid is added, equal to that needed to dissolve the carbonates, a solution with roughly equal concentrations of acetic acid and acetate ion will result. Such a solution is a good acid buffer, with a pH of about 5. The equilibrium involved in this buffering action is

$$HC_2H_3O_2(aq) + H_2O(l) \rightleftharpoons H_3O^+(aq) + C_2H_3O_2^-(aq) \qquad K = 1.8 \times 10^{-5} \qquad \text{(Eq. 40)}$$

Further addition or removal of H_3O^+ ion merely shifts this equilibrium to a new position wherein the concentration of H_3O^+ ion is not significantly changed from its original concentration.

Barium ion can be separated from calcium ion by selectively precipitating light yellow barium chromate, $BaCrO_4$, whose $K_{sp} = 1.8 \times 10^{-10}$. Even though calcium chromate, $CaCrO_4$, whose $K_{sp} = 7.1 \times 10^{-4}$, is sparingly soluble, there is a sufficient difference between the solubility product constants of these two chromates to allow a satisfactory separation, if care is taken while doing the experiment.

The establishment of the acetic acid/acetate buffer system is critical because the CrO_4^{2-} ion, used to precipitate Ba^{2+} ion, is involved in the following hydrogen-ion-dependent equilibrium in solution:

$$2\,CrO_4^{2-}(aq) + 2\,H_3O^+(aq) \rightleftharpoons Cr_2O_7^{2-}(aq) + 3\,H_2O(l) \qquad K = 4.0 \times 10^{14} \qquad \text{(Eq. 23)}$$

If the H_3O^+ ion concentration is very high, this equilibrium is shifted to the right; a higher $Cr_2O_7^{2-}$ ion concentration and a lower CrO_4^{2-} ion concentration result. Under these conditions of low CrO_4^{2-} concentration, not even $BaCrO_4$ will precipitate. When the H_3O^+ ion concentration is low (higher pH), the CrO_4^{2-} ion concentration in solution will increase as the equilibrium in Equation 34 is shifted toward the left. The CrO_4^{2-} ion concentration may become so large that the ion product of Ca^{2+} ion and CrO_4^{2-} ion will exceed the solubility product constant of $CaCrO_4$. If this happens, $CaCrO_4$ will also precipitate from solution. At a H_3O^+ ion concentration of 1.0×10^{-5} (pH of 5), the equilibrium concentration of CrO_4^{2-} ion is sufficient to precipitate $BaCrO_4$, but not $CaCrO_4$, from a solution that is approximately $0.10M$ in each cation.

A light yellow precipitate formed during the above separation is most likely $BaCrO_4$ and may confirm the presence of Ba^{2+} ion. However, because $CaCrO_4$ is also yellow and may precipitate, particularly if the pH is too high, a further confirmation reaction is necessary. Barium and its volatile salts produce a characteristic yellow-green color when heated in a flame. Because $BaCrO_4$ is not sufficiently volatile to give a good flame test, the $BaCrO_4$ must be converted to barium chloride ($BaCl_2$) with $12M$ HCl. The chromate ion oxidizes a portion of the added Cl^- ion in strongly acid solution, thus dissolving the $BaCrO^4$, as shown in Equations 41 and 42. A sample of the solution is placed in the flame. If Ba^{2+} ion is present, it imparts a characteristic yellow-green color to the flame. Under the reaction conditions in this experiment, the color can be difficult to see. The Cr^{3+} ion (derived from the dissolved CrO_4^{2-} ion) does not impart color to a flame.

$$BaCrO_4(s) \rightleftharpoons Ba^{2+}(aq) + CrO_4^{2-}(aq) \qquad \text{(Eq. 41)}$$

$$16\,H_3O^+(aq) + 2\,CrO_4^{2-}(aq) + 6\,Cl^-(aq) \rightleftharpoons 2\,Cr^{3+}(aq) + 3\,Cl_2(aq) + 24\,H_2O(l) \qquad \text{(Eq. 42)}$$

C. Separating and Confirming Calcium

The supernatant liquid remaining after $BaCrO_4$ has been precipitated contains Ca^{2+} ion. Upon addition of oxalate ion ($C_2O_4^{2-}$) to this solution, white calcium oxalate (CaC_2O_4) precipitates, as shown in Equation 43.

$$Ca^{2+}(aq) + C_2O_4^{2-}(aq) \rightleftharpoons CaC_2O_4(s, \text{white}) \qquad K_{sp} = 2.0 \times 10^{-9} \qquad \text{(Eq. 43)}$$

Although any white precipitate formed at this point is most likely to be CaC_2O_4 and may confirm the presence of Ca^{2+} ion, barium oxalate (BaC_2O_4) whose $K_{sp} = 1.7 \times 10^{-7}$, is also white and may precipitate if Ba^{2+} ion was not completely removed earlier.

Most oxalates are soluble in concentrated acid because $C_2O_4^{2-}$ ion is the anion of the moderately weak organic acid, oxalic acid (HOOCCOOH). In concentrated acid, CaC_2O_4 dissolves, as shown in Equation 44, as does BaC_2O_4.

$$CaC_2O_4(s) + 2\,H_3O^+(aq) \rightleftharpoons Ca^{2+}(aq) + H_2C_2O_4(aq) + 2\,H_2O(l) \qquad \text{(Eq. 44)}$$

A further confirmation reaction is necessary. The white precipitate is dissolved in a small amount of $6M$ HCl, and a flame test is employed. If Ca^{2+} ion is present, it imparts a characteristic brick red color to the flame.

IV. Flame Tests

Detailed instructions on preparing and performing a flame test are found under **Some Notes on Semimicro Technique**. In brief, a sample of a volatile salt of the alkaline earth metal is placed on a piece of clean inert wire, the wire is inserted into a Bunsen burner flame, and the color imparted to the flame is observed.

The detail of what happens in the Bunsen burner flame is complex and not completely understood. It is known that in both the alkaline earth atoms and the alkaline earth compounds present in the flame, valence electrons are excited to states of higher energy by the thermal energy of the flame. As these excited species move to a cooler portion of the flame, the excited electrons return to a lower energy state by emitting radiant energy of discrete and characteristic frequencies. For many of the alkaline earth metals and alkali metals, the emitted radiant energy includes frequencies that are in the visible region of the electromagnetic spectrum. Hence, characteristic colors are observed in flame tests. Practical use is made of this phenomenon by adding these salts to fireworks to produce variously colored displays.

In this experiment, you will separate Fe^{3+}, Ni^{2+}, Cr^{3+}, Ba^{2+}, and Ca^{2+} ions from a solution known to contain these ions. You will verify the presence of each cation, using a confirmation reaction. Then, you will determine the cations present in an unknown solution containing one or more of these five cations, following the same procedure used with the known cation solution.

PROCEDURE

Some Notes on Semimicro Technique

1. *Precipitations:* The precipitating reagent should be added dropwise with stirring until precipitation is complete.

2. *Completeness of Precipitation:* So that interfering cations are not left in solution, it is often necessary, where noted, to allow the precipitate to settle in the test tube or to centrifuge the supernatant liquid and the precipitate, and then carefully add 1 additional drop of reagent. If more precipitate forms, a few more drops of reagent should be added and the above procedure repeated until no further precipitation is observed.

3. *Washing Precipitates:* To ensure removal of interfering ions from moist precipitates, it is necessary, where noted, to wash the precipitate. This procedure involves decanting the supernatant liquid, adding the required amount of specified wash liquid to the tube containing the moist precipitate, mixing the precipitate and wash liquid thoroughly with a clean glass stirring rod, centrifuging, and, decanting and discarding the wash liquid.

CAUTION

A solution in a small test tube cannot be heated safely over a direct flame.

4. *Heating a Solution:* Placing the test tube containing the solution to be heated in a hot or boiling water bath is generally a preferred method.

5. *Removing Supernatant Liquids:* Liquids over precipitates are most often removed by careful decantation. However, the supernatant liquid can be carefully withdrawn with a small medicine dropper, or pipet, if necessary.

Occasionally a precipitate does not centrifuge completely. To fully separate a supernatant liquid in such a situation, twist a small piece of cotton batting to a point and insert it partway into the tip of the clear eye-dropper, leaving a tuft extending outside the tip. Draw up the supernatant liquid through the cotton, which will filter out the floating particles of precipitate. Enough precipitate should remain in the test tube for testing of those cations. Carefully remove the cotton and release the clear supernatant liquid into a clean 10×75-mm test tube.

6. *Flame Tests:* Dip a clean loop of Nichrome or platinum wire into a solution of the ion to be tested. The flame test is easier to observe if there is a film of solution spanning the loop because more material will be in the flame. Place the wire loop in a nonluminous, blue Bunsen burner flame. Note the color imparted by the substance adhering to the loop. Some cations, such as Ba^{2+} and Ca^{2+}, produce colors that are visible for only a very short time. Thus, it may be necessary to repeat the flame test several times to be certain of the color produced by the ion being tested.

The wire loop may be cleaned by dipping the wire into $6M$ HCl contained in a small test tube and then heating the wire in a blue Bunsen burner flame until the wire is red hot. If the wire imparts a color to the flame due to impurities adhering to its surface, then the wire should be redipped into the $6M$ HCl and reheated in a Bunsen burner flame until red hot. This cleaning procedure must be repeated until the wire imparts no significant color to the Bunsen burner flame. The HCl solution should be discarded following the directions of your laboratory instructor.

I. Separating Selected Group III Cations and Group IV Cations

Figure 2 is a flowchart showing the separation and identification of the selected Group III and IV cations Cr^{3+}, Fe^{3+}/Fe^{2+}, Ni^{2+}, Ba^{2+}, and Ca^{2+} ions.

CHEMICAL ALERT

$6M$ acetic acid—toxic and corrosive
$6M$ ammonia—toxic and irritant
$0.2M$ ammonium oxalate—irritant
$0.1M$ barium chloride—highly toxic
$0.1M$ calcium chloride—irritant
$0.1M$ chromium(III) chloride—toxic and irritant
$6M$ hydrochloric acid—toxic and corrosive
3% hydrogen peroxide—corrosive
$0.1M$ iron(III) chloride—toxic and corrosive
$0.1M$ nickel(II) chloride—toxic, irritant, and suspected carcinogen
$6M$ nitric acid—toxic, corrosive, and strong oxidant
$0.1M$ potassium chromate—suspected carcinogen
$0.1M$ potassium thiocyanate—irritant
$1M$ thioacetamide—toxic and carcinogen

CAUTION

Wear departmentally approved eye protection while doing this experiment.

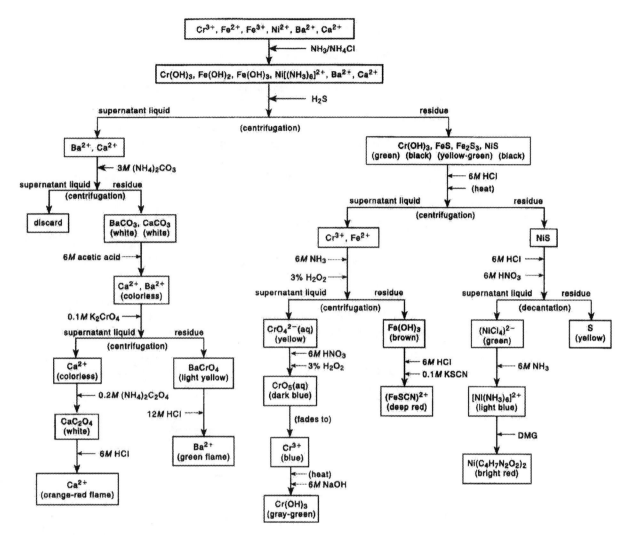

Figure 2
Flowchart for separating Groups III and IV ions

II. Separating and Confirming Group III Cations, Chromium(III), Iron(III), and Nickel(II)

A. Precipitating Selected Group III Cations

> **CAUTION**
>
> **6M hydrochloric acid is a corrosive, toxic solution that can cause burns. Prevent contact with your eyes, skin, and clothing. Avoid inhaling vapors and ingesting the solution.**

Add 2 drops of 6M HCl to 15 drops of the known Group III and IV cation solution (Cr^{3+}, Fe^{3+}, Ni^{2+}, Ba^{2+}, and Ca^{2+} ions) in a 75-mm test tube. Add sufficient 6M NH_3 dropwise to make the solution just alkaline to litmus paper. Then add 5 drops of 6M NH_3 in excess. Thoroughly stir the solution with a clean glass stirring rod. This operation will produce a NH_3/NH_4^+ ion buffer system in the appropriate pH range to precipitate $Fe(OH)_3$ and $Cr(OH)_3$.

CAUTION

Thioacetamide has proven to be a carcinogen in animal feeding studies. It is safe to use if handled prudently. Avoid skin contact with the thioacetamide solution. Wash your hands thoroughly with soap or detergent after using the solution.

Add 10 drops of $1M$ thioacetamide solution to the test tube, and heat the tube and its contents for 10 min in a boiling water bath. Centrifuge the tube and its contents for 2 min, and save the supernatant liquid by decanting it into a clean 75-mm test tube. Label this test tube, which contains Group IV ions.

CAUTION

$6M$ ammonia water is a corrosive, toxic solution. Prevent contact with your eyes, skin, and clothing. Avoid inhaling vapors and ingesting the solution.

Use 15 drops of $6M$ NH_3 to wash the precipitate remaining in the test tube. Agitate the precipitate with the wash solution by stirring with a clean glass stirring rod and recentrifuge the tube and its contents for 2 min.

NOTE: In all parts of this experiment, follow the directions of your laboratory instructor for discarding reaction mixtures and unused reagents.

Decant and discard the supernatant wash liquid. Save the precipitate in the test tube. Record your observations on Data Sheet 1.

B. Separating and Confirming Chromium(III)

Add 10 drops of $6M$ HCl to the precipitate in the test tube. Use a clean glass stirring rod to thoroughly stir the contents of the tube. Heat the tube and its contents in a boiling water bath for 2 min. Centrifuge the tube and its contents for 2 min. Decant the supernatant liquid, containing the Fe^{2+} and Cr^{3+} ions, into a 75-mm test tube.

If the supernatant liquid is not free of NiS precipitate particles, filter the precipitate from the liquid, using the following procedure. Twist a small tuft of cotton to a point. Insert the cotton partway into the small end of a medicine dropper. Draw the solution through the cotton, remove the cotton, and place the filtered supernatant liquid in a clean 75-mm test tube. Wash the NiS precipitate with 15 drops of distilled water, thoroughly stir the mixture with a clean glass stirring rod, and centrifuge for 1 min. Discard the washings and save the precipitate of NiS for further manipulations.

Take the supernatant liquid containing Fe^{2+} and Cr^{3+} ions, and while stirring with a clean glass stirring rod add sufficient $6M$ NH_3 to make the supernatant strongly basic to pH indicator paper.

CAUTION

3% hydrogen peroxide solution is an oxidant and a corrosive solution that can cause burns. Prevent contact with your eyes, skin, and clothing. Avoid ingesting the solution.

Add 5 drops of 3% H_2O_2 solution to the alkaline supernatant liquid. Thoroughly stir the contents of the test tube using a clean glass stirring rod. Allow the mixture to stand for 0.5 min. Then *destroy* unreacted H_2O_2 by heating the tube and its contents in a water bath for 3 min or until the evolution of gas bubbles subsides. Centrifuge the tube and its contents for 1 min. If the supernatant liquid is not yellow, check the pH of the solution. If it is strongly basic, continue. If it is not strongly basic, add more $6M$ NH_3, and repeat the addition and destruction of 3% H_2O_2.

Decant and save the supernatant liquid, containing the CrO_4^{2-} ion, in a 125-mm test tube. Save the precipitate of $Fe(OH)_3$ in a 75-mm test tube for confirmation of the presence of Fe^{3+} ion.

CAUTION ⚠️

$6M$ nitric acid is a corrosive, toxic solution that can cause severe burns. Prevent contact with your eyes, skin, and clothing. Avoid inhaling vapors and ingesting the solution.

Add $6M$ HNO_3 dropwise until the solution is acidic to pH paper (pH 3). Add 1 drop of 3% H_2O_2 solution. Heat the mixture to boiling. Observe the results for 0.5 min. Unreacted H_2O_2 in acidic solution is not destroyed by heating.

CAUTION ⚠️

$6M$ sodium hydroxide solution is a corrosive, toxic solution that can cause burns. Prevent contact with your eyes, skin, and clothing. Avoid ingesting the solution.

Cool the tube and its contents under tap water, and add $6M$ NaOH solution dropwise. If the solution turns dark blue or yellow indicating the presence of CrO_5 or CrO_4^{2-} ion, H_2O_2 is still present. Add $6M$ HNO_3 until the color fades. Repeat the addition of $6M$ NaOH solution. When all the H_2O_2 has decomposed, add $6M$ NaOH solution dropwise until the solution is basic to pH indicator paper. Record your observations on Data Sheet 1.

C. Confirming Iron(III)

Dissolve the precipitate of $Fe(OH)_3$, which you saved from the separation of Cr^{3+} ion, by adding 5 drops of $6M$ HCl. Stir the solution with a clean glass stirring rod. Add a volume of distilled water equal to that of the solution in the test tube. Add 5 drops of $0.1M$ potassium thiocyanate (KSCN) solution, and stir. Record your observations on Data Sheet 1.

D. Confirming Nickel(II)

Add 4 drops of $6M$ HCl and 6 drops of $6M$ HNO_3 to the NiS precipitate saved in the test tube. Heat the test tube and its contents for 2 min. The black precipitate should dissolve, leaving the Ni^{2+} ion in solution. A small dark residue of sulfur and unreacted sulfide may remain and can be discarded after decanting the acidic cation solution into a clean 75-mm test tube.

Add sufficient $6M$ NH_3 to make the solution alkaline to litmus. If a slight precipitate of $Fe(OH)_3$ appears, centrifuge the tube and its contents for 1 min. Decant the supernatant liquid into a clean 75-mm test tube. Add 5 drops of dimethylglyoxime (DMG) solution to the supernatant liquid. Thoroughly stir the contents with a clean glass stirring rod. Allow the tube and its contents to stand for 1 min. If no precipitate forms, check the pH to make sure the solution is basic. Record your observations on Data Sheet 1.

III. Separating and Confirming Selected Group IV Cations, Barium(II) and Calcium(II)

A. Precipitating Group IV Cations

The supernatant liquid from the initial Group III precipitation contains the Group IV cations. Add 15 drops of $3M$ ammonium carbonate, $(NH_4)_2CO_3$, solution to the liquid in the test tube. Use a clean glass stirring rod to thoroughly stir the contents of the test tube, then centrifuge for 2 min. Decant and discard the supernatant liquid. Wash the precipitate in the test tube with 15 drops of distilled water. Thoroughly stir the contents again and centrifuge again for 2 min. Decant and discard the wash liquid, and save the precipitate in the test tube. Record your observations on Data Sheet 2.

B. Separating and Confirming Barium(II)

> **CAUTION** ⚠
>
> **$6M$ acetic acid is a corrosive solution that can cause burns. Prevent contact with your eyes, skin, and clothing. Avoid inhaling vapors and ingesting the solution.**

Dissolve the carbonate precipitate from Part *A* by adding 5 drops of $6M$ acetic acid to the test tube and its contents. Heat the tube and its contents for 30 s in a boiling water bath. Stir the contents with a clean glass stirring rod. Add 2 additional drops of $6M$ acetic acid, if necessary, to completely dissolve the precipitate. To the clear solution in the test tube, add 3 additional drops of $6M$ acetic acid. Then add 10 drops of $0.1M$ potassium chromate (K_2CrO_4) solution. Stir the contents of the tube with a clean glass stirring rod. Heat the tube and its contents for 1 min in a boiling water bath. While the mixture is still hot, centrifuge it for 2 min. Decant the supernatant liquid into a 75-mm test tube. Save the liquid for confirmation of the presence of Ca^{2+} ion. Save the precipitate in the test tube for the flame test for Ba^{2+} ion. Record your observations on Data Sheet 2.

Wash the precipitate obtained above with 15 drops of distilled water. Centrifuge the tube and its contents for 2 min and decant. Discard the supernatant liquid. Add 5 drops of $12M$ HCl to the precipitate in the test tube. Heat the tube and its contents for 2 min in a boiling water bath. Perform a flame test on the clear solution thus obtained. Dip a clean wire loop in the Ba^{2+} ion solution and place the loop in a Bunsen burner flame. Record the color of the flame on Data Sheet 2.

C. Separating and Confirming Calcium(II)

Add 10 drops of $0.2M$ ammonium oxalate, $(NH_4)_2C_2O_4$, solution to the supernatant liquid from the chromate precipitation in Part B. Thoroughly stir the contents of the test tube with a clean glass stirring rod, and centrifuge for 2 min. Decant and discard the supernatant liquid. Wash the precipitate with two 15-drop portions of distilled water. Note your observations on Data Sheet 2.

Further confirmation of Ca^{2+} ion may be obtained by dissolving the precipitate in 3 drops of 6M HCl. Perform a flame test on the resulting Ca^{2+} ion solution. Record the color of the flame on Data Sheet 2.

IV. Analyzing a Group III and IV Unknown Cation Solution

Obtain a solution containing one or more of the Group III and/or IV cations from your laboratory instructor. Record the unknown identification number on Data Sheet 3.

Repeat the procedure in Sections II and III with this solution. Report on Data Sheet 3 the cations you found in your solution. Record evidence to support the presence of the cations you reported.

If the unknown solution is part of a general unknown originally containing ions from other groups, perform the preceding steps with 15 drops of the supernatant liquid from the initial precipitation of the Group II cations. If the unknown test solution is the supernatant liquid from the Group II precipitation in acidic H_2S solution, then there will probably be residual H_2S remaining in solution.

When such a solution is made alkaline, the S^{2-} ion equilibrium concentration will increase, causing an immediate appearance of a Group III sulfide precipitate. Even though such a precipitate forms, it is still necessary to perform all of the steps outlined in the procedure for the precipitation of Group III ions, to ensure complete precipitation of these ions.

CAUTION

Wash your hands thoroughly with soap or detergent before leaving the laboratory.

Name _Section_ _Date_

Post-Laboratory Questions

(Use the spaces provided for the answers and additional paper if necessary.)

1. Chromium(III) hydroxide is highly insoluble in distilled water but dissolves readily in either acidic or basic solution. Briefly explain why the compound can dissolve in acidic or in basic but not in neutral solution. Write appropriate equations to support your answer.

2. Explain how dissolving the Group IV carbonate precipitate with $6M$ CH_3COOH, followed by the addition of extra acetic acid, establishes a buffer with a pH of approximately 5.

3. A solution contains either Cr^{3+} or Ni^{2+} ion. Describe a reaction with a single reagent that will identify which ion is present.

4. The addition of S^{2-} ion to $Fe(OH)_2(s)$ results in the formation of $FeS(s)$. Explain why the addition of S^{2-} ion to $Cr(OH)_3(s)$ does not result in the formation of $Cr_2S_3(s)$.

5. A black precipitate remaining from the separation of Cr^{3+} and Fe^{2+} ions from Ni^{2+} ion is dissolved in HCl and HNO_3. Some NH_3 is added, followed by several drops of dimethylglyoxime.

(1) A colorless solution results. What do you think has happened?

(2) What might have gone wrong?

6. A student was analyzing an unknown containing only Group IV cations. When the unknown was treated with $3M$ $(NH_4)_2CO_3$ solution, a white precipitate formed. Because the acetic acid bottle was empty, the student used $6M$ HCl to dissolve the precipitate. Following the procedure of this experiment, the student then added $0.10M$ K_2CrO_4 solution as directed, and no precipitate formed. Oxalic acid was added to the solution, and no precipitate formed.

(1) What mistake did the student make?

(2) How did the mistake affect the tests for the cations in solution?

Name   Section   Date

Data Sheet 1

(Record below all observations made while performing Section II of this experiment.)

II. Separating and Confirming Selected Group III Cations

A. Precipitating selected Group III cations

B. Separating and confirming chromium(III)

C. Confirming iron(III)

D. Confirming nickel(II)

Data Sheet 2

(Record all observations made while performing Section III of this experiment.)

III. Separating and Confirming Selected Group IV Cations

A. Precipitating Group IV cations

B. Separating and confirming barium(II)

Flame color, barium(II)

C. Separating and confirming calcium(II)

Flame color, calcium(II)

Data Sheet 3

IV. Analyzing a Group III and IV Unknown Cation Solution

unknown identification number _____

cations found _____   _____

_____   _____

_____   _____

Attach a separate sheet of paper presenting evidence proving the presence of listed cations.

_____   _____   _____
Name   Section   Date

Pre-Laboratory Assignment

1. Read an authoritative source for a discussion of the techniques to be used in this experiment.

2. Safety is a very important aspect of experimental design.

(1) Explain why it would be dangerous to pour 100 mL of a 0.10M $Cr(NO_3)_3$ solution into the drain.

(2) Suggest a way that Cr^{3+} ion could be removed from the solution as a solid, so that the solution could be disposed of and the solid sent to a chemical landfill.

3. A solid is known to be either $BaCO_3$ or $CaCO_3$. It is dissolved in 6M acetic acid. A pale yellow precipitate forms when K_2CrO_4 solution is added. The subsequent flame test with that precipitate shows an orange-red color. Which cation is present? Briefly explain.

4. There are several procedures in this experiment that involve oxidation–reduction reactions.

   (1) Using your chemistry textbook as a reference, briefly explain what is meant by the terms "oxidation" and "reduction." Write appropriate equations to support your answer.

   (2) In different steps in this experiment, hydrogen peroxide (H_2O_2) serves as an oxidizing agent or as a reducing agent. Write equations for the reactions involved. What is the major difference between the conditions of the two reactions?

5. Write equations for the following separations. Indicate any conditions required for the reactions to occur, such as pH 5.

   (1) Group III cations from Group IV cations.

   (2) Fe^{2+} and Cr^{3+} ions from Ni^{2+} ion.

(3) Fe^{2+} ion from Cr^{3+} ion.

(4) Ba^{2+} ion from Ca^{2+} ion.

6. Nickel(II) ion is a Group III cation. The compound $Ni(OH)_2(s)$ is very insoluble in water; the K_{sp} of $Ni(OH)_2$ is 2.0×10^{-16}. Nevertheless, $Ni(OH)_2(s)$ does not precipitate from a basic solution that contains ammonia. Briefly explain this behavior. Write appropriate equations to support your answer.

The Chemistry and Qualitative Analysis of Anions

Prepared by James G. Boyles, Bates College, and
Judith C. Foster and David S. Page, Bowdoin College

PURPOSE OF THE EXPERIMENT

Develop the chemistry of selected anions, including Cl^-, Br^-, I^-, SO_4^{2-}, CO_3^{2-}, SO_3^{2-}, PO_4^{3-}, NO_2^-, and NO_3^- ions. Use this chemistry to develop an analysis procedure for solutions containing these anions.

BACKGROUND INFORMATION

I. Classes of Reactions and Chemical Processes

In this experiment, you will be performing a number of chemical reactions and observing the results. Some of the important types of chemical reactions and processes you will be conducting are summarized below.

Acid–base reactions occur when an ion reacts with either hydronium ion (H_3O^+) or hydroxide ion (OH^-) in aqueous solution. No oxidation or reduction is involved. For example

$$SO_4^{2-}(aq) + H_3O^+(aq) \rightleftharpoons HSO_4^-(aq) + H_2O(l) \qquad \text{(Eq. 1)}$$

Hydrolysis reactions take place when the elements of one or more moles of water react with an ion or compound. For example

$$Fe^{3+}(aq) + 6H_2O(l) \rightleftharpoons Fe(OH)_3(s, \text{rusty}) + 3H_3O^+(aq) \qquad \text{(Eq. 2)}$$

Oxidation–reduction reactions occur when one reagent containing an element with a high electron affinity reacts with a second reagent containing an element of lower electron affinity. The oxidizing agent (high electron affinity) gains electrons from the reducing agent (lower electron affinity). The oxidizing agent is reduced and the reducing agent is oxidized. For example

$$2I^-(aq) + Cl_2(aq) \rightleftharpoons I_2(aq) + 2Cl^-(aq) \qquad \text{(Eq. 3)}$$

Disproportionation reactions are a special form of oxidation–reduction reactions. In a disproportionation reaction, the same species serves as an electron donor (reducing agent) and electron acceptor (oxidizing agent). Some of the species are oxidized and some are reduced, the exact proportions depending on the oxidation number of the oxidized and reduced species relative to the original reactant. This is also called **autoredox** (self-oxidation and self-reduction). For example

$$3\,HNO_2(aq) \rightleftharpoons 2\,NO(aq) + NO_3{}^-(aq) + H_3O^+(aq) \qquad \text{(Eq. 4)}$$

Decomposition occurs when an unstable compound or ion spontaneously decomposes into one or more new products. For example

$$H_2CO_3(aq) \rightleftharpoons H_2O(l) + CO_2(aq) \qquad \text{(Eq. 5)}$$

Oxidation–reduction may also be involved in the decomposition (as shown in Equation 4).

Precipitation occurs when the ion product of ions in solution exceeds the solubility product constant, K_{sp}, of the compound formed by a combination of these ions. This results in the formation of a solid, or precipitate. For example

$$Ag^+(aq) + Cl^-(aq) \rightleftharpoons AgCl(s,\ white) \qquad \text{(Eq. 6)}$$

The **ion product** is the value obtained when the actual concentrations of ions in solution are substituted into the K_{sp} expression.

Dissolution occurs when the ion product of the dissolved species is less than the K_{sp} of the solid, resulting in the solid dissolving. Often, an added reagent reacts with one of the ions formed in the dissolution, lowering the ion product and shifting the equilibrium in favor of the dissolution. For example

$$Ag_2CO_3(s,\ white) + 2\,H_3O^+(aq) \rightleftharpoons 2\,Ag^+(aq) + 3\,H_2O(l) + CO_2(aq) \qquad \text{(Eq. 7)}$$

Extraction is not, strictly speaking, a chemical reaction, but it is a chemical process. It involves the migration of chemical species from one layer to another of a multi-phase system of immiscible solvents. Often, one solvent is aqueous and another is organic, as is the case in this experiment. The migration from one phase to another occurs because the species is more soluble in one solvent than in the other. For example

$$I_2(aq,\ yellow) \rightleftharpoons I_2(organic,\ violet) \qquad \text{(Eq. 8)}$$

In this experiment, extraction is used to identify certain compounds that have similar colors in aqueous solution but very different colors when extracted into an organic solvent, methylene chloride (CH_2Cl_2). This color change is due to differences in solvent–solute interaction.

II. Chemistry of Selected Anions

A. Sulfate Ion ($SO_4{}^{2-}$)

In aqueous solution, the following equilibria involving $SO_4{}^{2-}$ ion are established.

$$SO_4{}^{2-}(aq) + H_2O(l) \rightleftharpoons HSO_4{}^-(aq) + OH^-(aq) \qquad K_b = 1.0 \times 10^{-12} \qquad \text{(Eq. 9)}$$

$$HSO_4^-(aq) + H_2O(l) \rightleftharpoons H_2SO_4(aq) + OH^-(aq) \quad K_b = 1.0 \times 10^{-15} \qquad \text{(Eq. 10)}$$

K_b is the **base dissociation constant** for the reactions shown in Equations 9 and 10. As the constants for these equilibria indicate, SO_4^{2-} ion is a very weak Brønsted base, and hydrogen sulfate ion (HSO_4^-, bisulfate ion) is a relatively strong acid. Sulfate ion undergoes negligible hydrolysis. Therefore, SO_4^{2-} ion is stable in acidic and basic solutions.

Most sulfates are water soluble, but two notable exceptions are lead(II) sulfate ($PbSO_4$) and barium sulfate ($BaSO_4$), as shown in Equations 11 and 12.

$$PbSO_4(s, \text{white}) \rightleftharpoons Pb^{2+}(aq) + SO_4^{2-}(aq) \quad K_{sp} = 1.4 \times 10^{-8} \qquad \text{(Eq. 11)}$$

$$BaSO_4(s, \text{white}) \rightleftharpoons Ba^{2+}(aq) + SO_4^{2-}(aq) \quad K_{sp} = 1.1 \times 10^{-10} \qquad \text{(Eq. 12)}$$

The affinity of SO_4^{2-} ion for protons in aqueous solution is so small, as seen in Equation 9, and the solubility product constants of $PbSO_4$ and $BaSO_4$ are so small, that these salts are classified as insoluble sulfates even in moderately strong acid solutions. The formation of the white, acid-insoluble precipitate of $BaSO_4$ upon addition of a source of barium ion (Ba^{2+}) to a solution is a reliable classification reaction for the presence of SO_4^{2-} ion.

Sulfate ion is neither a strong oxidizing nor a strong reducing agent and therefore is not involved in significant redox reactions.

B. Sulfite Ion (SO_3^{2-})

In aqueous solution, SO_3^{2-} ion is involved in the following equilibria.

$$SO_3^{2-}(aq) + H_2O(l) \rightleftharpoons HSO_3^-(aq) + OH^-(aq) \quad K_b = 1.8 \times 10^{-7} \qquad \text{(Eq. 13)}$$

$$HSO_3^-(aq) + H_2O(l) \rightleftharpoons H_2SO_3(aq) + OH^-(aq) \quad K_b = 1.0 \times 10^{-12} \qquad \text{(Eq. 14)}$$

$$H_2SO_3(aq) \rightleftharpoons H_2O(l) + SO_2(aq) \qquad \text{(Eq. 15)}$$

Sulfite ion is a weak Brønsted base, but hydrolysis (see Equations 13 and 14) does give basic solutions. These equilibria are shifted strongly to the right in highly acidic solutions (low pH). Sulfurous acid (H_2SO_3), as such, has never been isolated. If an acidified solution containing SO_3^{2-} ion is heated, sulfur(IV) oxide (SO_2, sulfur dioxide) gas is evolved, because the solubility of SO_2 decreases with increasing temperature.

Sulfur(IV) oxide is a colorless gas with characteristic choking fumes with a sharp odor. Consequently its presence, even in small amounts, is easily detected. An acceptable procedure for determining the presence of SO_3^{2-} ion in a solution is to acidify and heat the solution, and carefully check for the odor of SO_2.

The sulfites of most cations are insoluble in water, with the notable exceptions being the sulfites of ammonium ion (NH_4^+) and the alkali metal cations. The insolubility of barium sulfite ($BaSO_3$) will play an important role in this experiment. Sulfite ion has a much stronger affinity for a proton than does SO_4^{2-} ion, as you can see from the magnitude of the equilibrium constants of the reactions in Equations 9 and 13. Consequently, sulfites, which are insoluble in water, are at least moderately soluble in acidic solutions. Their dissolution is accompanied by the evolution of SO_2 gas.

Sulfite ion is easily oxidized to SO_4^{2-} ion by atmospheric oxygen. When a solution is left standing for a long time, SO_3^{2-} ion in the solution may be converted almost entirely to SO_4^{2-} ion, as shown in Equation 16.

$$2\,SO_3^{2-}(aq) + O_2(g) \rightleftharpoons 2\,SO_4^{2-}(aq) \qquad \text{(Eq. 16)}$$

Many reducing agents will reduce SO_3^{2-} ion to elemental sulfur, S(s), or even to hydrogen sulfide (H_2S), where sulfur is in the -2 oxidation state. Thus, SO_3^{2-} ion can act as either an oxidizing or a reducing agent.

C. Nitrate Ion (NO_3^-)

Nitrate ion is the anion of a strong Brønsted acid and undergoes negligible hydrolysis in aqueous solution. Nitrate ion can exist in significant concentration in both acidic and basic solutions.

No insoluble inorganic salts are formed with NO_3^- ion.

The nitrogen in NO_3^- ion is in its highest possible oxidation state $(+5)$, hence NO_3^- ion can react only as an oxidizing agent, resulting in the reduction of the nitrogen. In redox reactions involving NO_3^- ion, there can be a variety of products, but for a given system only one product predominates. The concentration of NO_3^- ion and the acidity of the solution largely determine the identity of the product. For example, only the following redox reaction occurs in strongly acidic solutions.

$$NO_3^-(aq) + 4\,H_3O^+(aq) + 3\,Fe^{2+}(aq) \rightleftharpoons NO(aq) + 3\,Fe^{3+}(aq) + 6\,H_2O(l) \qquad \text{(Eq. 17)}$$

This reaction can form the basis for a useful confirmatory reaction. The product, nitrogen(II) oxide (NO, nitric oxide), which is dissolved in the solution, can be released from the reaction mixture as NO gas by heating. This release shifts the equilibrium of Equation 17 to the right. Gaseous NO in the presence of oxygen (O_2) from the air is oxidized rapidly to gaseous nitrogen(IV) oxide (NO_2, nitrogen dioxide), which is readily detected as a red-brown gas with an antiseptic odor.

$$2\,NO(g, \text{colorless}) + O_2(g) \rightleftharpoons 2\,NO_2(g, \text{red-brown}) \qquad \text{(Eq. 18)}$$

Thus, when a strongly acidic solution containing NO_3^- ion is heated in the presence of a reducing agent such as iron(II) ion (Fe^{2+}, ferrous ion), a rapid reaction occurs, accompanied by the evolution of a red-brown gas, which serves as a confirmatory reaction for NO_3^- ion. An intermediate product is usually seen. As NO is produced, the unstable complex ion, pentaaquonitrosyliron(II), $[Fe(H_2O)_5(NO)]^{2+}$, briefly colors the solution dark brown. This ion decomposes as the NO(aq) is converted to NO(g), which evolves from the solution on heating.

D. Nitrite Ion (NO_2^-)

In aqueous solution, NO_2^- ion is involved in the following equilibrium:

$$NO_2^-(aq) + H_2O(l) \rightleftharpoons HNO_2(aq) + OH^-(aq) \quad K_b = 2.2 \times 10^{-11} \qquad \text{(Eq. 19)}$$

As the equilibrium constant for this hydrolysis reaction indicates, NO_2^- ion is a very weak Brønsted base and undergoes negligible hydrolysis.

Upon addition of H_3O^+ ion, the equilibrium in Equation 19 shifts far to the right. This shift greatly increases the concentration of HNO_2. Pure nitrous acid has never been isolated, and in warm aqueous solutions it decomposes, via disproportionation, as shown in Equation 20.

$$3\,HNO_2(aq) \;\rightleftharpoons\; 2\,NO(aq) + NO_3^-(aq) + H_3O^+(aq) \qquad \text{(Eq. 20)}$$

When an acidified solution containing NO_2^- ion is heated, NO gas, formed from the disproportionation, is evolved, because its solubility decreases with increasing temperature. Nitrogen(II) oxide is a colorless gas that reacts rapidly with atmospheric oxygen to produce red-brown NO_2 gas.

$$2\,NO(g,\ colorless) + O_2(g) \rightleftharpoons 2\,NO_2(g,\ red\text{-}brown) \qquad \text{(Eq. 18)}$$

Thus, a convenient procedure for determining the presence of NO_2^- ion in a solution would be to acidify and heat the solution and to look for red-brown NO_2 gas with an antiseptic odor.

The nitrites of most cations are soluble in water, with the notable exception of silver nitrite ($AgNO_2$). With the exception of the alkali-metal nitrites, all solid nitrites decompose on heating.

Nitrite ion is a weak reducing agent and can be oxidized to NO_3^- ion only by strong oxidizing agents such as permanganate ion (MnO_4^-) and basic hydrogen peroxide (H_2O_2). Nitrite ion is a reasonably strong oxidizing agent. It is reduced to NO by such reducing agents as SO_3^{2-}, H_2S, Fe^{2+} and I^- (iodide) ions.

Nitrite ion reacts similarly to NO_3^- ion in strongly acidic media. A differentiation between NO_2^- ion and NO_3^- ion can be made, however, because an acidic solution containing NO_2^- ion requires no reducing agent to produce the red-brown NO_2 gas.

E. Carbonate Ion (CO_3^{2-})

In aqueous solution, CO_3^{2-} ion is involved in the following equilibria:

$$CO_3^{2-}(aq) + H_2O(l) \;\rightleftharpoons\; HCO_3^-(aq) + OH^-(aq) \quad K_b = 2.0 \times 10^{-4} \qquad \text{(Eq. 21)}$$

$$HCO_3^-(aq) + H_2O(l) \;\rightleftharpoons\; H_2CO_3(aq) + OH^-(aq) \quad K_b = 2.5 \times 10^{-8} \qquad \text{(Eq. 22)}$$

$$H_2CO_3(aq) \;\rightleftharpoons\; H_2O(l) + CO_2(aq) \qquad \text{(Eq. 23)}$$

Carbonate ion is a moderately strong Brønsted base and undergoes considerable hydrolysis in aqueous solution. The predominant species present is determined by the pH of the solution. At pH 11, CO_3^{2-} ion is the predominant species; at pH 8, hydrogen carbonate ion (HCO_3^-, bicarbonate) is most abundant; at pH 4 and lower, carbonic acid (H_2CO_3) and its decomposition products, carbon(IV) oxide (CO_2, carbon dioxide) and H_2O, are dominant. Therefore, if acid is added to a carbonate-containing solid or solution, CO_2, a colorless, odorless gas, will be evolved, because the equilibria in Equations 21, 22, and 23 are shifted to the right.

The barium and calcium salts of carbonates are insoluble in distilled water. Because the addition of H_3O^+ ion will shift the equilibrium shown in Equations 21, 22, and 23 strongly to the right, both substances are quite soluble in acid solutions. Their dissolution is accompanied by the evolution of CO_2 gas.

$$BaCO_3(s,\ white) \rightleftharpoons Ba^{2+}(aq) + CO_3^{2-}(aq) \quad K_{sp} = 5.0 \times 10^{-9} \qquad (Eq.\ 24)$$

$$CaCO_3(s,\ white) \rightleftharpoons Ca^{2+}(aq) + CO_3^{2-}(aq) \quad K_{sp} = 7.5 \times 10^{-9} \qquad (Eq.\ 25)$$

Thus, a convenient reaction for the presence of CO_3^{2-} ion in a solution is to acidify the solution and to observe CO_2 evolution, noting the lack of odor. Many common cations form insoluble carbonates, notable exceptions being those of NH_4^+ ion, sodium ion (Na^+), and potassium ion (K^+).

Neither CO_3^{2-} ion nor HCO_3^- ion is a strong oxidizing or reducing agent. These ions are not involved in significant redox reactions.

F. Phosphate Ion (PO_4^{3-})

The following equilibria are established in aqueous solution containing PO_4^{3-} ion:

$$PO_4^{3-}(aq) + H_2O(l) \rightleftharpoons HPO_4^{2-}(aq) + OH^-(aq) \quad K_b = 1.0 \times 10^{-2} \qquad (Eq.\ 26)$$

$$HPO_4^{2-}(aq) + H_2O(l) \rightleftharpoons H_2PO_4^-(aq) + OH^-(aq) \quad K_b = 1.6 \times 10^{-7} \qquad (Eq.\ 27)$$

$$H_2PO_4^-(aq) + H_2O(l) \rightleftharpoons H_3PO_4(aq) + OH^-(aq) \quad K_b = 1.3 \times 10^{-12} \qquad (Eq.\ 28)$$

Phosphate ion is a reasonably strong Brønsted base and hydrolyzes appreciably to form a basic solution containing PO_4^{3-} ion, hydrogen phosphate ion (HPO_4^{2-}), dihydrogen phosphate ion ($H_2PO_4^-$), and orthophosphoric acid (H_3PO_4). The ratio of these species in aqueous solution is determined by the pH of the solution.

Most phosphates, except those of the alkali metals, are sparingly soluble in neutral solution. Examples of these sparingly soluble phosphates are barium phosphate, $Ba_3(PO_4)_2$, calcium phosphate, $Ca_3(PO_4)_2$, silver phosphate, Ag_3PO_4, lead(II) phosphate, [$Pb_3(PO_4)_2$, plumbous phosphate], bismuth phosphate, $BiPO_4$, and iron(II) phosphate [$Fe_3(PO_4)_2$, ferrous phosphate]. These substances are soluble in strongly acidic solutions, because the PO_4^{3-} ion produced can become involved in the hydrolysis reactions shown in Equations 26, 27, and 28.

Phosphorus is in its highest possible oxidation state (+5) in PO_4^{3-} ion, hence PO_4^{3-} ion can react only as an oxidizing agent, because the phosphorus can only be reduced. In aqueous solution, PO_4^{3-} ion is a very weak oxidizing agent and can be reduced only under rather strong reducing conditions. Redox reactions are not an important part of aqueous PO_4^{3-} ion chemistry.

Phosphate ion forms an insoluble bright yellow precipitate when treated with ammonium molybdate, $(NH_4)_2MoO_4$, in an acidic solution.

$$PO_4^{3-}(aq) + 3\,NH_4^+(aq) + 12\,MoO_4^{2-}(aq) + 24\,H_3O^+(aq)$$

$$\rightleftharpoons (NH_4)_3PMo_{12}O_{40}(s,\ bright\ yellow) + 36\,H_2O(l) \qquad (Eq.\ 29)$$

The precipitate, ammonium molybdophosphate, $(NH_4)_3PMo_{12}O_{40}$, or ammonium phosphomolybdate, varies in composition, but the P to Mo ratio remains constant at 1 to 12. This reaction is quite sensitive and can be used to confirm the presence of PO_4^{3-} ion. Arsenate ion (AsO_4^{3-}) gives a similar precipitate, but only if the solution is heated strongly.

G. Chloride (Cl^-), Bromide (Br^-), and Iodide (I^-) Ions

As anions of strong Brønsted acids, Cl^-, Br^-, and I^- undergo negligible hydrolysis in aqueous solution. The halide ions are stable in aqueous solution over a broad pH range, encompassing both acidic and basic solutions.

Most halide salts are soluble, notable exceptions being those of silver, lead(II), and mercury(I). Indeed, precipitation of Cl^-, Br^-, or I^- ion as a silver salt is a common first step in the identification of halide ions. Because of the negligible hydrolysis of the halides, the silver halides are insoluble even in strongly acidic solution, except HCl.

$$AgCl(s, white) \rightleftharpoons Ag^+(aq) + Cl^-(aq) \quad K_{sp} = 1.2 \times 10^{-10} \qquad \text{(Eq. 30)}$$

$$AgBr(s, cream) \rightleftharpoons Ag^+(aq) + Br^-(aq) \quad K_{sp} = 4.8 \times 10^{-13} \qquad \text{(Eq. 31)}$$

$$AgI(s, light\ yellow) \rightleftharpoons Ag^+(aq) + I^-(aq) \quad K_{sp} = 1.4 \times 10^{-16} \qquad \text{(Eq. 32)}$$

The colors of these three substances are so similar that a confirmation reaction is needed to distinguish them from one another. Because these three halides have only one negative oxidation state, -1, they are capable of acting only as reducing agents. The decreasing relative strengths of the halide ions as reducing agents is: $I^- > Br^- > Cl^-$. Hence, the decreasing relative strengths of their oxidized forms, as the neutral diatomic halogens, as oxidizing agents is: $Cl_2 > Br_2 > I_2$. Therefore, chlorine (Cl_2) will oxidize Br^- ion to elemental bromine (Br_2) and will oxidize I^- ion to elemental iodine (I_2). Bromine will only oxidize I^- ion to I_2.

$$Cl_2(aq, colorless) + 2\,Br^-(aq) \rightleftharpoons Br_2(aq, yellow\text{-}brown) + 2\,Cl^-(aq) \qquad \text{(Eq. 33)}$$

$$Cl_2(aq, colorless) + 2\,I^-(aq) \rightleftharpoons I_2(aq, yellow\text{-}brown) + 2\,Cl^-(aq) \qquad \text{(Eq. 34)}$$

Because the colors of $Br_2(aq)$ and $I_2(aq)$ are very similar, we need a further reaction to distinguish them. We will take advantage of the fact that bromine and iodine have very different colors when dissolved in the organic solvent methylene chloride (CH_2Cl_2). Methylene chloride is much less polar than water, so the nonpolar halogens dissolve preferentially in the less polar solvent. Methylene chloride and water are not mutually soluble, and CH_2Cl_2, being denser than water (1.33 g mL^{-1}), will form the lower layer. [If hexane (C_6H_{14}), density 0.66 g mL^{-1}, is used in place of CH_2Cl_2, it will form the upper layer.] The halogen reactions occur in the aqueous layer. When the two layers are vigorously mixed by shaking, the halogen product will migrate into the CH_2Cl_2 layer (or C_6H_{14} layer). Upon separation, the color of the organic layer will be distinctive for each halogen.

Bromine dissolves in CH_2Cl_2 to give a solution of red-amber color, and iodine dissolves in CH_2Cl_2 to give a solution of violet color. This color difference can be used in a confirmatory reaction. Chlorine does not impart any color to CH_2Cl_2.

The formation of an acid-insoluble precipitate following the addition of aqueous silver nitrate ($AgNO_3$) to an unknown solution indicates the presence of one or more of the halide ions. Positive identification of the anion can be achieved by reacting the precipitate with the oxidizing agent, Cl_2 (as chlorine water), and CH_2Cl_2, followed by thorough shaking of the solution. Observation of the color imparted to the CH_2Cl_2 layer will confirm the presence of a given halide ion in the original solution. If the CH_2Cl_2 layer is colorless, Cl^- ion was present initially. If the CH_2Cl_2 layer is redamber, Br^- ion was present. If the CH_2Cl_2 layer is violet, I^- ion was present.

Be careful when interpreting the observations, because the reaction for Cl^- ion results in two colorless layers. This reaction is only a negative confirmation reaction, and is only to be used if the classification reaction indicates a halide. Almost all other anions except Br^- and I^- ions will also yield two colorless layers with this reaction. If both steps of the $AgNO_3$ reaction indicate the presence of a halide, then do the CH_2Cl_2 confirmatory reaction.

In this experiment, you will observe the behavior of known anions with a number of reagents. Then you will determine which anion is present in each of the unknown samples assigned to you. Initially, you will use three classification reactions to determine to which group of anions your anion belongs. These reactions are:

(1) formation of insoluble barium salts, such as $BaCO_3$, $BaSO_4$, $BaSO_3$, and $Ba_3(PO_4)_2$;

(2) formation of volatile products when H_3O^+ ion is added to such anions as CO_3^{2-}, NO_2^-, and SO_3^{2-} ions; and

(3) formation of insoluble silver salts, such as $AgBr$, $AgCl$, and AgI.

Then, you will do the confirmatory reactions suggested by the results of your elimination reactions.

PROCEDURE

CHEMICAL ALERT

0.5M ammonium molybdate—toxic and irritant
0.1M barium chloride—highly toxic
chlorine water—toxic, irritant, and oxidant
dichloromethane—toxic and irritant
hexane—flammable and irritant
1M iron(II) sulfate—toxic
3M nitric acid—toxic, corrosive, and strong oxidant
0.1M silver nitrate—toxic, corrosive, and oxidant
sodium carbonate—irritant
sodium chloride—irritant
sodium hydrogen phosphate—irritant
sodium iodide—irritant
sodium nitrate—toxic, irritant, and oxidant
sodium nitrite—toxic and oxidant
sodium sulfate—irritant
sodium sulfite—irritant
sulfuric acid—toxic and corrosive

Wear departmentally approved eye protection while doing this experiment.

In this investigation, you will use solid samples as sources of the anion for analysis. The use of a large amount of salt in any given reaction is neither necessary nor desirable. In the following procedure, references to "an amount" of a given salt should be taken to mean a portion of solid approximately equal in bulk to a grain of rice. You should first perform the experiments using known samples, as instructed. After completing the procedure with the known samples of anions, use the reactions given in the **Procedure** to identify the anion in each of several unknown salts. To avoid contamination, rinse your spatula and stirring rod with distilled or deionized water after every use.

NOTE: In all parts of this experiment, follow the directions of your laboratory instructor for discarding reaction mixtures and unused reagents.

I. Classification Reactions

It is convenient to categorize the anions being studied in terms of several types of chemical reactions.

A. Barium Salts Insoluble in Distilled Water (SO_4^{2-}, SO_3^{2-}, CO_3^{2-}, and PO_4^{3-} Ions)

Dissolve an amount of solid sodium sulfate (Na_2SO_4) in 10 drops of distilled water in a 75-mm test tube. Add 5 drops of $0.1M$ barium chloride ($BaCl_2$) solution.

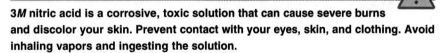

$3M$ nitric acid is a corrosive, toxic solution that can cause severe burns and discolor your skin. Prevent contact with your eyes, skin, and clothing. Avoid inhaling vapors and ingesting the solution.

Stir the solution, and then add 5 drops of $3M$ HNO_3. Stir thoroughly. Note the color and odor of any gas evolved. Record your observations on Data Sheet 1. Repeat this procedure using solid sodium sulfite (Na_2SO_3), sodium carbonate (Na_2CO_3), and sodium phosphate (Na_3PO_4) as anion samples. In each case, record your observations on Data Sheet 1.

B. Anions Forming Volatile Products (SO_3^{2-}, CO_3^{2-}, and NO_2^- Ions)

Dissolve an amount of solid Na_2SO_3 in 5 drops of distilled water in a 75-mm test tube.

$3M$ sulfuric acid is a corrosive, toxic solution that can cause severe burns. Prevent contact with your eyes, skin, and clothing. Avoid ingesting the solution.

Add 5 drops of $3M$ H_2SO_4 to the tube. Carefully note the odor and color of any gas evolved. The color can be noted by holding the tube against a white background. If necessary, gently heat the tube and its contents in a warm water bath. Record your observations on Data Sheet 1.

Repeat the procedure with a solid sample of Na_2CO_3 and with a sample of sodium nitrite ($NaNO_2$). In each case, record your observations on Data Sheet 1.

C. Silver Salts Insoluble in Distilled Water and in Acid Solution (Cl^-, Br^-, and I^- ions)

Dissolve an amount of sodium chloride (NaCl) in 10 drops of distilled water in a 75-mm test tube.

CAUTION ⚠️

0.1 M silver nitrate is a toxic solution that can cause skin burns or discolor your skin. Prevent contact with your eyes, skin, and clothing. If any of the solution comes in contact with your skin, wash immediately with copious amounts of water, and notify your laboratory instructor.

Add to this solution 5 drops of 0.1M $AgNO_3$ solution. Stir thoroughly. Next, add 5 drops of 3M HNO_3, and stir thoroughly. Record your observations on Data Sheet 1.

Repeat this procedure with solid samples of sodium bromide (NaBr) and of sodium iodide (NaI). In each case, record your observations on Data Sheet 1.

II. Confirmatory Reactions

Each of the following reactions is used to confirm the presence of a given anion.

A. Sulfate Ion (SO_4^{2-})

Dissolve an amount of Na_2SO_4 in 10 drops of distilled water in a 75-mm test tube. Add 5 drops of 0.1M $BaCl_2$ solution. Stir the contents of the tube. Add 5 drops of 3M HNO_3 to the mixture and stir thoroughly. Record your observations on Data Sheet 2.

B. Sulfite Ion (SO_3^{2-})

Dissolve an amount of Na_2SO_3 in 5 drops of distilled water in a 75-mm test tube. Add 5 drops of 3M H_2SO_4 and stir thoroughly. Carefully note the odor and color of any gas evolved. If necessary, gently heat the tube and its contents in a warm water bath. Record your observations on Data Sheet 2.

C. Nitrate Ion (NO_3^-)

Dissolve an amount of $NaNO_3$ in 5 drops of a 1M solution of iron(II) sulfate ($FeSO_4$, ferrous sulfate), available as 1M $FeSO_4$ in 1M H_2SO_4, in a 75-mm test tube. Add 3–5 drops of concentrated H_2SO_4. The tube and its contents will become warm. This reaction should occur without stirring.

Be sure that the mouth of the test tube is not pointing toward anyone, because a gas may be evolved rapidly. If necessary, gently heat the tube and its contents in a warm water bath for 1 min or until a reaction has taken place. Record your observations on Data Sheet 2.

D. Nitrite Ion (NO_2^-)

Dissolve an amount of $NaNO_2$ in 5 drops of distilled water in a 75-mm test tube. Carefully add 5 drops of $3M$ H_2SO_4. If necessary, gently heat the tube and its contents in a warm water bath. Record your observations on Data Sheet 2.

E. Carbonate Ion (CO_3^{2-})

Place an amount of Na_2CO_3 in 5 drops of distilled water in a 75-mm test tube. Add 5 drops of $3M$ H_2SO_4. Note the odor and color of any gas evolved. Record your observations on Data Sheet 2.

F. Phosphate Ion (PO_4^{3-})

Dissolve an amount of Na_3PO_4 in 8 drops of $3M$ nitric acid in a 75-mm test tube. Add 4 drops of $0.5M$ $(NH_4)_2MoO_4$ solution. Stir thoroughly. Record your observations on Data Sheet 2.

G. Halide Ions (Cl^-, Br^-, and I^-)

Dissolve an amount of $NaCl$ in 5 drops of distilled water in a 75-mm test tube. Add 10 drops of chlorine water, and then 10 drops of CH_2Cl_2. Stopper the tube, and shake the tube and its contents thoroughly. Note the color of the CH_2Cl_2 (lower) layer. Record your observations on Data Sheet 2.

Repeat this procedure using $NaBr$ and using NaI. In each case, record your observations on Data Sheet 2.

III. Analyzing Unknowns

Obtain from your laboratory instructor several unknown samples to identify. Record the number of your samples on Data Sheet 3. Each sample will contain only one anion. For each sample, perform *all three* classification reactions, even if the first or second one appears positive. Then, perform those confirmatory reactions suggested by the results of the classification reactions. Record your observations on Data Sheet 3, and report the identity of each unknown anion.

CAUTION

Wash your hands thoroughly with soap or detergent before leaving the laboratory.

Name   Section   Date

Post-Laboratory Questions

(Use the spaces provided for the answers and additional paper if necessary.)

1. Suppose that a solution is tested for NO_2^- ion by adding $3M$ H_2SO_4 and heating, repeating this process until no further reaction occurs. This solution is then analyzed for NO_3^- ion by adding $FeSO_4$ solution and more H_2SO_4, heating the test tube and its contents. The NO_3^- ion reaction is positive. In this case, is it accurate to state that NO_3^- ion was present in the original solution? Briefly explain. Write appropriate equations to support your answer.

2. A solution contains a mixture of Cl^- and Br^- ions. Can both be positively identified? Briefly explain. Write appropriate equations to support your answer.

3. The solubility product constants of AgCl, AgBr, and AgI are, respectively, 1.7×10^{-10}, 4.1×10^{-13}, and 1.5×10^{-16}. The K_{sp} expression for each silver halide, AgX, is:

$$K_{sp} = [Ag^+][X^-]$$

When the ion product, $[Ag^+][X^-]$, exceeds the K_{sp}, AgX(s) will precipitate until the ion product once again equals K_{sp}. If the Ag^+ ion concentration in the mixture is $0.067M$ (diluted from $0.1M$), calculate the detection limit of this reaction for each halide, the value below which there will be no observed reaction.

4. A solution is known to contain Cl^-, NO_3^-, NO_2^-, and SO_4^{2-} ions. Which of these ions can be positively identified? Describe the reactions used and the results.

5. Why wouldn't HCl be a good acid to use to determine the solubility of a silver precipitate in acid solution?

Name _____   *Section* _____   *Date* _____

Data Sheet 1

(Record below your observations made while performing Section I of this experiment.)

I. Classification Reactions

A. Barium salts insoluble in distilled water	B. Anions forming volatile products	C. Silver salts insoluble in distilled water and in acid solution
sulfate	sulfite	chloride
sulfite	carbonate	bromide
carbonate	nitrite	iodide
phosphate		

Data Sheet 2

(Record below your observations made while performing Section II of this experiment.)

II. Confirmatory Reactions

bromide	carbonate	chloride
iodide	nitrate	nitrite
phosphate	sulfate	sulfite

Data Sheet 3

III. Analyzing Unknowns

unknown identification number _____

   1. Classification reactions performed and observed results

   2. Confirmatory reactions performed and observed results

   3. Equations for the reactions performed that led to the identification of the unknown

   4. Identity _____

_____

unknown identification number _____

1. Classification reactions performed and observed results

2. Confirmatory reactions performed and observed results

3. Equations for the reactions performed that led to the identification of the unknown

4. Identity _____

_____

unknown identification number _____

1. Classification reactions performed and observed results

2. Confirmatory reactions performed and observed results

3. Equations for the reactions performed that led to the identification of the unknown

4. Identity _____

_____

_____   _____   _____
Name   Section   Date

Pre-Laboratory Assignment

1. Of the following anions, Br^-, CO_3^{2-}, Cl^-, I^-, NO_3^-, NO_2^-, PO_4^{3-}, SO_4^{2-} and SO_3^{2-}, list those ions that meet the following criteria.

(1) Gives a precipitate with Ag^+ ion that is insoluble in HNO_3.

(2) Is involved in an oxidation–reduction reaction as part of a confirmation reaction.

(3) Gives a precipitate with Ba^{2+} ion that is soluble in HNO_3.

(4) Evolves a gas when acid is added.

(5) Releases an odorous gas as a product.

(6) Does not produce a precipitate in any classification or confirmatory reaction described in this experiment.

2. What types of reactions are involved when acid is added to a solution containing SO_3^{2-} ion, resulting in the release of gaseous SO_2?

3. In analyzing an unknown salt containing one of the anions discussed in this module, a student obtains negative results for all three classification reactions. Briefly explain.

4. A solution is known to contain at least one of the anions discussed in this module.

   (1) The yellowish precipitate that forms when $AgNO_3$ solution is added to the solution dissolves when HNO_3 is added. Which anion(s) may be present?

   (2) A $BaCl_2$ solution is added to this solution. A white precipitate forms that dissolves when HNO_3 is added. No color, odor, or evolved gas is observed. Which anion is present? Describe a confirmatory reaction for this anion.

5. In some of the classification reactions, it is important when there is *no* reaction upon addition of a second reagent. For which anions is this true?

Studying Electrochemical Half-Cells and Half-Reactions

Prepared by Henry D. Schreiber, Virginia Military Institute, James N. Spencer, Franklin and Marshall College, and H. Anthony Neidig, Lebanon Valley College

PURPOSE OF THE EXPERIMENT:

Construct three half cells. Write equations for the half-reactions and net oxidation–reduction reactions for your half-cells. Determine net potentials for the half-cells. Rank the three metals studied according to ease of oxidation.

BACKGROUND INFORMATION

Oxidation–Reduction Reactions

If we place a strip of nickel metal (Ni) in copper(II) sulfate solution ($CuSO_4$), we can see immediate evidence of a chemical reaction. The Ni begins to dissolve, and a deposit of metallic copper, Cu, appears on the Ni strip.

We can divide this reaction into two parts, one involving nickel and the other, copper. In the first part, Ni dissolves into solution as the nickel(II) ion, Ni^{2+}. In this reaction, each nickel atom releases two electrons, as shown in Equation 1:

$$Ni(s) \rightarrow Ni^{2+}(aq) + 2\,e^- \qquad \text{(Eq. 1)}$$

At the same time, copper(II) ions (Cu^{2+}) form Cu. This process consumes electrons, as shown by Equation 2:

$$Cu^{2+}(aq) + 2\,e^- \rightarrow Cu(s) \qquad \text{(Eq. 2)}$$

The reactant that *releases* electrons, Ni in this case, is said to be **oxidized**. The reactant that *gains* electrons, Cu^{2+} ion here, is **reduced**.

We express the overall reaction by adding the oxidation of Ni described by Equation 1 to the reduction of Cu^{2+} ion described by

Equation 2. The net reaction involves the transfer of electrons from Ni to Cu^{2+} ion, as shown in Equation 3.

$$Ni(s) + Cu^{2+}(aq) \rightarrow Ni^{2+}(aq) + Cu(s) \qquad \text{(Eq. 3)}$$

Reactions that involve the transfer of electrons from one reactant to another are called **oxidation–reduction** or **redox** reactions. Equations 1 and 2 are individually called the oxidation and reduction **half-reactions**, respectively, because each constitutes half of the overall reaction. The electrons appearing in Equations 1 and 2 cancel when we add the half-equations to yield the overall equation (Equation 3). In any oxidation–reduction reaction equation, the number of electrons released by the oxidation half-reaction must equal the number of electrons consumed by the reduction half-reaction.

If we place a strip of Cu in nickel(II) sulfate solution ($NiSO_4$), we observe no evidence of a reaction. This shows that the reverse of the reaction in Equation 3 does not occur spontaneously. Thus, we may conclude that Cu^{2+} ion has a greater tendency to accept electrons from Ni than Ni^{2+} ion does to accept electrons from Cu. In other words, Cu^{2+} ion has a greater **reduction potential** than Ni^{2+} ion.

By testing different combinations of metals and aqueous solutions of metal salts, we can arrange metal ions in order of their relative reduction potentials. Table 1 ranks selected metal ions by **standard reduction potentials**, determined under standard conditions: 25 °C, 1 atm, and 1 mol L^{-1} ion concentration. The standard reduction potential, E°_{red}, measured in

Table 1 *Selected standard reduction potentials for half-reactions*

Reduction half-equation	E°_{red}, V
$Mg^{2+}(aq) + 2\,e^- \rightarrow Mg(s)$	−2.37
$Al^{3+}(aq) + 3\,e^- \rightarrow Al(s)$	−1.66
$Cr^{2+}(aq) + 2\,e^- \rightarrow Cr(s)$	−0.91
$Zn^{2+}(aq) + 2\,e^- \rightarrow Zn(s)$	−0.76
$Fe^{2+}(aq) + 2\,e^- \rightarrow Fe(s)$	−0.44
$Ni^{2+}(aq) + 2\,e^- \rightarrow Ni(s)$	−0.26
$Sn^{2+}(aq) + 2\,e^- \rightarrow Sn(s)$	−0.14
$Pb^{2+}(aq) + 2\,e^- \rightarrow Pb(s)$	−0.13
$2\,H^+(aq) + 2\,e^- \rightarrow H_2(g)$	0.00
$Cu^{2+}(aq) + 2\,e^- \rightarrow Cu(s)$	+0.34
$Ag^+(aq) + e^- \rightarrow Ag(s)$	+0.80

volts (V), provides a quantitative measure of a metal ion's tendency to accept electrons. The reference point for reduction potentials, 0.000 V, has been arbitrarily assigned to hydronium ions (H_3O^+) in aqueous solution being reduced to hydrogen gas (H_2). The greater the reduction potential, the greater the tendency for reduction. Table 1 shows that Cu^{2+} ion does indeed have a greater reduction potential than Ni^{2+} ion, as we concluded from the experiment described previously.

The half-reactions that represent the oxidation of the metals in Table 1 to their respective metal ions are the reverse of the half-reactions in Table 1. The **standard oxidation potential, E^o_{oxid},** of an oxidation half-reaction has the same numerical value, but the opposite sign, of the corresponding standard reduction potential. For example, the reduction potential of magnesium ion, Mg^{2+}, is -2.37 V, so the oxidation potential of Mg is $+2.37$ V. This relatively large positive voltage indicates that Mg is a very reactive (or active) metal, one that readily donates electrons in an oxidation–reduction reaction. In contrast, silver metal, Ag, is not especially active, as indicated by its oxidation potential of -0.80 V.

To illustrate how we can use Table 1 to predict the spontaneity for specific oxidation–reduction reactions, let's predict what will happen if we place a Cu strip in silver(l) nitrate solution ($AgNO_3$) under standard conditions. We need to determine whether or not the Cu atoms will donate electrons to the silver ion, Ag^+, as part of a spontaneous oxidation–reduction reaction. The reduction half-reaction for Ag^+ ion is shown in Equation 4. The standard reduction potential for Ag^+ is $+0.80$ V (as shown in Table 1).

$$Ag^+(aq) + e^- \rightarrow Ag(s) \qquad \text{(Eq. 4)}$$

The oxidation half-reaction for Cu is shown in Equation 5. Cu has a standard oxidation potential of -0.34 V.

$$Cu(s) \rightarrow Cu^{2+}(aq) + 2\,e^- \qquad \text{(Eq. 5)}$$

To obtain the net equation, we add the equations for the two half-reactions. To equalize the number of electrons in the equations for each half-reaction, we must multiply Equation 4 by 2. Note that this manipulation does not change E^o_{red} for the reduction half-reaction. The net equation is shown in Equation 6.

$$
\begin{array}{ll}
2\,Ag^+(aq) + 2\,e^- \rightarrow 2\,Ag(s) & E^o_{red} = +0.80\,V \\
Cu(s) \rightarrow Cu^{2+}(aq) + e^- & E^o_{oxid} = -0.34\,V \\
\hline
2\,Ag^+(aq) + Cu(s) \rightarrow Cu^{2+}(aq) + 2\,Ag(s) & E^o_{net} = +0.46\,V \quad \text{(Eq. 6)}
\end{array}
$$

Because the **standard net potential (E^o_{net}),** or sum of the standard reduction and oxidation potentials, is positive for Equation 6, we predict that the reaction will occur spontaneously. In fact, a Cu strip does dissolve spontaneously in $AgNO_3$ solution, resulting in an Ag deposit on the Cu strip.

Similarly, for the reaction of Ni in $CuSO_4$ solution (Equation 3), we calculate the standard net potential to be $+0.60$ V. This positive net potential correlates with the observation of a spontaneous oxidation–reduction reaction between these reactants.

Electrochemical Cells

Remarkably, oxidation–reduction reactions can even occur between reactants in separate containers. In such cases, electrons are transferred from the reactant being oxidized to the reactant being reduced through a wire connecting the two containers.

For example, suppose we place a Ni strip in an aqueous nickel(II) salt solution. Then we place a Cu strip in an aqueous copper(II) salt solution in a separate container. Next, we connect one end of a wire to the Ni strip and the other end to the Cu strip. Electrons will pass through the wire from the Ni strip to the Cu strip, provided that we make an additional connection between the containers to complete the electrical circuit. This second connection is called a **salt bridge** and is shown in Figure 1. The entire assembly is an **electrochemical cell**, a system that utilizes a spontaneous oxidation–reduction reaction to pump electrons through an electrical circuit. An electrochemical cell is composed of two parts, or **half-cells**: in this case, a nickel half-cell, in which Ni is being oxidized, and a copper half-cell, in which Cu^{2+} ion is being reduced. The metal strips are called **electrodes**.

Electrons are driven from the nickel half-cell to the copper half-cell by the **net cell potential**, which is the sum of the reduction potential of Cu^{2+} ion and the oxidation potential of Ni. We can measure this force by connecting a voltmeter between the half-cells, as shown in Figure 1. The magnitude of the net cell potential and the direction of the electron flow through the wire depend on the relative potentials of the metal–metal ion couples for donating or accepting electrons, as summarized in Table 1. The net cell potential for our Ni–Cu cell indicates that the oxidation–reduction reaction is spontaneous and that the observed voltage should be +0.60 V under standard conditions.

In this experiment, you will place a zinc strip (Zn) in a $CuSO_4$ solution, a lead strip (Pb) in a $CuSO_4$ solution, and a Zn strip in a lead nitrate solution $Pb(NO_3)_2$. Then you will observe each chemical system. You will write equations for the half-reactions and a net equation for each system, calculate the net cell potential for each system, and predict whether or not the reaction would be spontaneous. Then you will rank the three metals by their relative ease of oxidation.

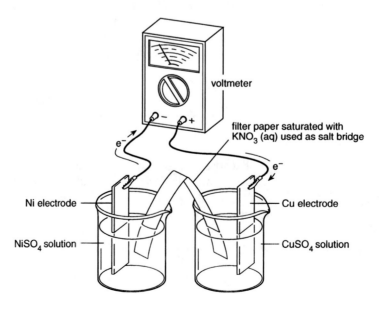

Figure 1

A typical electrochemical cell

Next, you will construct Zn–Cu and Fe–Cu electrochemical cells. The voltmeter for each cell should show a positive reading. For each cell, you will write equations for each of the half-reactions and the net cell reaction. Finally, you will calculate the standard net cell potential, based on the half-cell potentials in Table 1.

PROCEDURE

Chemical Alert

0.1M copper(II) sulfate solution—toxic and irritant

0.1M iron(II) sulfate solution—irritant

0.1M lead(II) nitrate solution—irritant and oxidant

0.5M potassium nitrate solution—irritant and oxidant

0.1M zinc(II) nitrate solution—irritant

CAUTION

Wear departmentally approved eye protection while doing this experiment.

I. Oxidation–Reduction Reactions

A. The Zn–Cu System

NOTE: Reaction indicators will be changes either in the appearance of the metal surfaces or the solutions. If the metal strips do not appear bright and shiny over their entire surfaces before the experiment, clean the surfaces with sandpaper.

1. Clean the surface of a Zn strip with sandpaper. Place the strip in a small test tube.

CAUTION

CuSO$_4$ is toxic and irritant. If any of the solution contacts your skin, thoroughly wash the area.

2. Transfer enough 0.1M CuSO$_4$ solution into the test tube to completely cover the Zn strip.

3. After 5 min, record your observations of the Zn–Cu^{2+} ion system on Data Sheet 1.

4. Place the used Zn strip in the container designated by your laboratory instructor and labeled "Discarded Zn Metal." Retain the CuSO$_4$ solution for use in Part B.

B. The Pb–Cu System

5. Clean a Pb strip with sandpaper if necessary. Place the strip in the CuSO$_4$ solution from Step 4.

6. After 5 min, record your observations of the Pb–Cu^{2+} ion system on Data Sheet 1.

7. Place the used Pb strip in the container provided by your laboratory instructor and labeled "Discarded Pb Metal." Pour the CuSO$_4$ solution

into the container provided by your laboratory instructor and labeled "Discarded CuSO₄ Solution."

C. The Zn–Pb System

8. Clean the surface of a Zn strip with sandpaper if necessary. Place the strip in a small test tube.

CAUTION

$Pb(NO_3)_2$ solution is toxic. If any of the solution contacts your skin, thoroughly wash the area.

9. Add $0.1M$ $Pb(NO_3)_2$ solution to the test tube until it covers the Zn strip.
10. After 5 min, record your observations of the $Zn–Pb^{2+}$ ion system on Data Sheet 1.
11. Place the used Zn strip in the container provided by your laboratory instructor and labeled "Discarded Zn Metal." Discard the $Pb(NO_3)_2$ solution into the container provided by your laboratory instructor and labeled "Discarded $Pb(NO_3)_2$ Solution."

II. Electrochemical Cells

A. The Zn–Cu Electrochemical Cell

12. Using a 25-mL graduated cylinder, measure 15 mL of $0.1M$ zinc(II) sulfate solution, $ZnSO_4$, and transfer it to a clean 20-mL beaker. Label the beaker "Zn."
13. Rinse your graduated cylinder and use it to measure 15 mL of $0.1M$ $CuSO_4$ solution and transfer it to another clean 20-mL beaker. Label the beaker "Cu."

NOTE: If the metal strips in Steps 14–16 do not appear bright and shiny over their entire surfaces, sand the metal surfaces until they are shiny.

14. If necessary, clean the surface of a Zn strip using sandpaper.
15. Connect one end of a Cu wire to the Zn strip, and place the strip in the beaker labeled "Zn." Make certain that the Cu wire does not contact the solution.
16. If necessary, clean the surface of a Cu strip using sandpaper. Attach one end of a Cu wire to the Cu strip, and place the strip in the beaker labeled "Cu." Do not allow the wire to contact the solution.
17. Pour about 50 mL of $0.5M$ potassium nitrate solution (KNO_3) into a clean 150-mL beaker.

NOTE: The filter paper saturated with KNO_3 solution serves as the salt bridge for the cell. The soaked paper makes contact between the half-cells in the two beakers. Do not allow the filter paper to become dry at any time during the experiment. If this should happen, resoak the filter paper with KNO_3 solution.

CAUTION

Potassium nitrate solution is an irritant and oxidant. If any of the solution contacts your skin, thoroughly wash the area.

18. Fold a piece of filter paper to about 1 cm wide. Place the filter paper in the KNO_3 solution. Allow the filter paper to become thoroughly soaked.

19. Position the soaked filter paper with tweezers or forceps so that one end of the paper is in the $CuSO_4$ solution and the other end is in the $ZnSO_4$ solution, as shown in Figure 1.

20. Connect the wire attached to the Zn strip to one voltmeter terminal. Connect the wire from the Cu strip to the other voltmeter terminal. Check the voltmeter reading. If the reading is negative, reverse the voltmeter connections.

21. Record the voltage registering on the voltmeter on Data Sheet 1.

22. Disconnect the Cu wires from the voltmeter and from the Zn strip. Remove the Zn strip and place it in the "Discarded Zn Metal" container. Pour the $ZnSO_4$ solution into the container provided by your laboratory instructor and labeled "Discarded $ZnSO_4$ Solution." Place the filter paper in the container labeled "Discarded Filter Paper." Leave the beaker labeled "Cu" intact.

B. The Fe–Cu Electrochemical Cell

23. After rinsing your 25-mL graduated cylinder, use it to measure 15 mL of a $0.1M$ iron(II) sulfate solution ($FeSO_4$), and pour the solution into a clean 20-mL beaker. Label the beaker "Fe."

24. If necessary, clean the surface of a Fe strip, using sandpaper. Attach one end of a Cu wire to the Fe strip, and place the strip in the $FeSO_4$ solution. Do not allow the Cu wire to contact the solution.

25. Prepare another salt bridge as in Step 18. Position the filter paper with forceps so that one end is in the $FeSO_4$ solution and the other end is in the $CuSO_4$ solution in the beaker labeled "Cu" from Part A.

26. Connect the wires attached to the Fe and Cu strips to the voltmeter terminals. Check the voltmeter reading. If the reading is negative, reverse the voltmeter connections.

27. Record the voltage registering on the voltmeter on Data Sheet 1.

28. Disconnect the wires from the voltmeter and the Fe and Cu strips. Place the strips in the containers provided by your laboratory instructor and labeled "Discarded Fe Metal" and "Discarded Cu Metal," respectively. Pour the $CuSO_4$, $FeSO_4$, and KNO_3 solutions into the containers labeled "Discarded $CuSO_4$ Solution," "Discarded $FeSO_4$ Solution," and "Discarded KNO_3 Solution," respectively. Place the filter paper in the "Discarded Filter Paper" container.

CAUTION

Wash your hands thoroughly with soap or detergent before leaving the laboratory.

CALCULATIONS

Do the following calculations and record the results on Data Sheet 2.

I. Oxidation–Reduction Reactions

A. The Zn–Cu System

1. Based on the fact that Zn atoms and Cu^{2+} ions are the only possible reactants in this system, write half-equations for the oxidation of Zn and the reduction of Cu^{2+} ion on the spaces provided on Data Sheet 2. Look up the potential for each half-equation in Table 1. Record these potentials on Data Sheet 2.

2. Write the net equation and determine the net potential. Predict whether or not this reaction is spontaneous, based on the sign of the net potential. Indicate whether or not your experimental observations are consistent with this prediction.

B. The Pb–Cu System

3. Write the half-equations and potentials for the reduction and oxidation that occur when Pb is added to $CuSO_4$ solution.

4. Add the half-equations and potentials to obtain the net reaction and net potential. Predict whether or not this reaction is spontaneous. Compare this prediction with your experimental observations for this system.

C. The Zn–Pb System

5. Write half-equations and potentials for the reduction and oxidation that occur when Zn is added to $PbNO_3$ solution.

6. Add the half-equations and potentials to obtain the net reaction and net potential. Predict whether or not this reaction is spontaneous. Compare this prediction with your experimental observations for this system.

D. Relative Scales of Reduction and Oxidation Potentials

7. Based on your experimental results, rank Zn^{2+}, Cu^{2+}, and Pb^{2+} ions in order of ease of reduction, easiest to hardest. Explain whether or not this ranking is consistent with the corresponding reduction potentials in Table 1.

8. Based on your experimental results, rank Zn, Cu, and Pb in order of ease of oxidation, easiest to hardest. Explain whether or not this ranking is consistent with the corresponding oxidation potentials in Table 1.

II. Electrochemical Cells

A. The Zn–Cu Electrochemical Cell

9. Write the half-equation for the half-reaction initiated in the beaker labeled "Cu." In order to determine whether Cu(s) is oxidized or Cu^{2+}(aq) is reduced in this half-equation, compare the two possible half-equations to those of Zn, in order to see which is preferentially oxidized and which is preferentially reduced, according to the half-cell potentials listed in Table 1.

10. Determine the half-equation for the half-reaction initiated in the beaker labeled "Zn."

11. Write the net cell reaction, and calculate the expected cell potential from the half-cell potentials listed in Table 1.

12. Compare the calculated cell potential to the measured voltage of the electrochemical cell.

B. The Fe–Cu Electrochemical Cell

13. Write the half-equation for the half-reaction initiated in the beaker labeled "Cu." Using Table 1, determine the half-cell potential for this half-equation.

14. Write the half-equation and the potential for the half-reaction initiated in the beaker labeled "Fe."

15. Determine the net cell reaction, and calculate the expected cell potential.

16. Compare the calculated cell potential to the measured voltage of the electrochemical cell.

_____   _____   _____
name   *section*   *date*

Post-Laboratory Questions

(Use the spaces provided for the answers and additional paper if necessary.)

1. A strip of tin (Sn) is placed in an $AgNO_3$ solution.

(1) Predict whether or not a spontaneous oxidation–reduction reaction should occur in this system. Explain your reasoning.

(2) Write a chemical equation to describe the net reaction, if it is spontaneous.

(3) Indicate the experimental observations you would expect for this procedure.

2. The half-cell reactions that occur in a typical flashlight battery are:

$$Zn(s) \rightarrow Zn^{2+}(aq) + 2\,e^-$$

$$2\,MnO_2(s) + Zn^{2+}(aq) + 2\,e^- \rightarrow ZnMn_2O_4(s)$$

Write a chemical equation describing the net cell reaction.

3. An electrochemical cell is constructed in which one half-cell contains $AgNO_3$ solution in contact with an Ag strip, and the other half-cell contains magnesium nitrate solution, $Mg(NO_3)_2$, in contact with a Mg strip. The two solutions are connected by a salt bridge, and the two metals are connected by a copper wire.

(1) Which ion, Mg^{2+} or Ag^+, is more easily reduced in aqueous solution?

(2) Write the half-equation for the reaction that occurs in the silver half-cell.

(3) Write the equation for the net cell reaction.

(4) Calculate the expected voltage for this cell.

_____ _____ _____
name   *section*   *date*

Data Sheet 1

I. Oxidation–Reduction Reactions

A. The Zn–Cu System
experimental observations:

B. The Pb–Cu System
experimental observations:

C. The Zn–Pb System
experimental observations:

II. Electrochemical Cells

A. The Zn–Cu Electrochemical Cell
cell voltage: _____

B. The Fe–Cu Electrochemical Cell
cell voltage: _____

_____   _____   _____
name   *section*   *date*

Data Sheet 2

I. Oxidation–Reduction Reactions

A. The Zn–Cu System

oxidation half-equation _____ $E^o_{oxid} =$ _____

reduction half-equation _____ $E^o_{red} =$ _____

net equation _____ $E^o_{net} =$ _____

prediction of spontaneity:

comparison of predicted spontaneity with experimental observations:

B. The Pb–Cu System

oxidation half-equation _____ $E^o_{oxid} =$ _____

reduction half-equation _____ $E^o_{red} =$ _____

net equation _____ $E^o_{net} =$ _____

prediction of spontaneity:

comparison of predicted spontaneity with experimental observations:

C. The Zn–Pb System

oxidation half-equation _____ $E^o_{oxid} =$ _____

reduction half-equation _____ $E^o_{red} =$ _____

net equation _____ $E^o_{net} =$ _____

prediction of spontaneity:

comparison of predicted spontaneity with experimental observations:

D. Relative Scales of Reduction and Oxidation Potentials

ranking of ions by ease of reduction, easiest to hardest:

comparison of ranking with ranking based on reduction potentials in Table 1:

ranking of ions by ease of oxidation, easiest to hardest:

comparison of ranking with ranking based on oxidation potentials in Table 1:

II. Electrochemical Cells

A. The Zn–Cu Electrochemical Cell

Cu half-cell equation _____ $E° =$ _____

Zn half-cell equation _____ $E° =$ _____

net cell equation _____ $E°_{net} =$ _____

comparison of observed and calculated cell voltages:

B. The Fe–Cu Electrochemical Cell

Cu half-cell reaction _____ $E° =$ _____

Fe half-cell reaction _____ $E° =$ _____

net cell reaction _____ $E°_{net} =$ _____

comparison of observed and calculated cell voltages:

name _____   _section_ _____   _date_ _____

Pre-Laboratory Assignment

(Use Table 1 as a source of half-equations and reduction potentials for this assignment.)

1. Rank the following metals by ease of oxidation, from hardest to easiest: Cu; aluminum, Al; Fe; and chromium, Cr.

2. An Al strip is placed in $CuSO_4$ solution.
   (1) Would you expect a spontaneous reaction to occur, based on the net potential?

   (2) If your answer to (1) is "yes," what would you observe?

   (3) Write a chemical equation that describes your predicted observations.

3. Describe what you would observe if you placed an Ag strip in an aluminum nitrate solution, $Al(NO_3)_3$.

4. Describe an electrochemical cell that would have the following net equation, by answering the following questions.

$$Fe(s) + Ni^{2+}(aq) \rightarrow Ni(s) + Fe^{2+}(aq)$$

(1) Write the reduction and oxidation half-equations for the cell.

(2) Sketch the electrochemical cell. Identify the components of the cell as in Figure 1.

(3) Calculate the expected net voltage for this cell.

Introducing Equilibrium

Prepared by H. Anthony Neidig, Lebanon Valley College, and
J. N. Spencer, Franklin and Marshall College

PURPOSE OF THE EXPERIMENT

Experimentally determine the effects of disturbances on chemical systems at equilibrium. Consider these effects in relation to Le Châtelier's principle.

BACKGROUND INFORMATION

Chemical equilibrium plays an important role in our lives. Many of the chemical changes involved in the metabolism of food are equilibrium-controlled processes. A number of important industrial processes involve chemical reactions that do not proceed to completion. Engineers must know how to manipulate such reactions in order to obtain the maximum yield of a desired product. A good example of an economically important equilibrium in manufacturing is the Haber process, used to produce ammonia.

Ammonia is a major fertilizer and is used in the synthesis of many nitrogen compounds. In the Haber process, nitrogen (N_2) reacts with hydrogen (H_2) to form ammonia (NH_3), as shown in Equation 1. The symbol in parentheses appearing after each substance in the equation describes the physical state of the preceding substance. The symbol (g) indicates that the substance is a gas, (*l*), a liquid, and (s), a solid; (aq) indicates that the substance is dissolved in water, forming an aqueous solution.

$$N_2(g) + 3\,H_2(g) \rightarrow 2\,NH_3(g) \qquad \text{(Eq. 1)}$$

Under the same conditions, NH_3 decomposes into N_2 and H_2, as shown in Equation 2.

$$2\,NH_3(g) \rightarrow N_2(g) + 3\,H_2(g) \qquad \text{(Eq. 2)}$$

At the same time reactants are forming products (Equation 1), some products are undergoing a chemical change to form reactants (Equation 2). The product, NH_3, is formed by the **forward reaction** (Equation 1), and NH_3 decomposes to form N_2 and H_2 in the **reverse reaction** (Equation 2). Reactions in which reactants are not completely converted to products because of the occurrence of the reverse reaction are called **reversible**

reactions. Such reactions are identified by a double arrow ($\rightleftharpoons$) in the equation describing the reaction, as shown in Equation 3.

$$N_2(g) + 3H_2(g) \rightleftharpoons 2NH_3(g) \qquad\qquad (Eq.\ 3)$$

Chemical systems that involve reversible reactions are in a dynamic state of constant interchange of reactant and product species. When the rate of the forward reaction (Equation 1) is equal to the rate of the reverse reaction (Equation 2), the system has reached a state of **equilibrium.** At equilibrium, the amounts of each substance in the system remain unchanged, even though the forward and reverse reactions are occurring constantly.

A change in any of the variables associated with a system at equilibrium may cause the equilibrium to be disturbed. We refer to such a change as a **stress** on the equilibrium state. When stress occurs, the system adjusts, or shifts, to accommodate the disturbance. This shift continues until a new equilibrium state is established.

We can predict the response of a chemical system at equilibrium to various stresses using **Le Châtelier's principle.** According to this principle, if a stress is applied to a system at equilibrium, the system will respond by shifting in the direction that reduces the stress, in order to reach a new equilibrium state.

Consider the effect of an increase in the amount of N_2 on the system at equilibrium shown in Equation 3. The added N_2 creates a stress on the equilibrium state. We can qualitatively describe the system's response to the added N_2, using Le Châtelier's principle. To reduce the stress, some of the added N_2 reacts with H_2 to form additional NH_3. Consequently, when a new equilibrium state is established, there is a greater amount of NH_3 than was present in the original equilibrium state. We commonly say that the addition of N_2 to the equilibrium system causes the equilibrium *to shift to the right;* that is, the amount of products increases and the amount of reactants decreases. This shift continues until the rates of the forward and reverse reactions are again equal and a new equilibrium state is reached.

On the other hand, if we add NH_3 to the system at equilibrium shown in Equation 3, the equilibrium will shift to the *left.* When the system reaches its new equilibrium state, it will have greater amounts of N_2 and H_2 than were present in the original equilibrium state.

Another means of disturbing a chemical system at equilibrium is to reduce the amount of one of the components. For instance, we could reduce the amount of NH_3 in the system at equilibrium represented by Equation 3. The system would respond by shifting to the right, to replenish NH_3 and establish a new equilibrium state. In the Haber process, the yield of NH_3 is increased by removing the NH_3 as it forms.

Another stress on a chemical system at equilibrium is a change in temperature. Such a change can be considered to be equivalent to adding or removing heat from the system. If the forward reaction is **exothermic,** meaning that heat is released as a product of the forward reaction, a temperature increase will cause the equilibrium to shift to the left. If the reaction is **endothermic,** meaning that heat is absorbed as a reactant in the forward reaction, a temperature increase will cause the equilibrium to shift to the right.

For example, the reaction in Equation 3 is exothermic. Heat is released as a product of the forward reaction. A temperature increase causes the equilibrium to shift to the left, resulting in a reduced amount of NH_3 and increased amounts of N_2 and H_2.

In this experiment, you will study the responses of several chemical systems at equilibrium to different kinds of stress. First, you will consider the equilibrium between chromate ion (CrO_4^{2-}) and dichromate ion ($Cr_2O_7^{2-}$). The **net ionic equation** for this equilibrium, which shows only the reacting species, is given in Equation 4. This system is formed by dissolving potassium chromate (K_2CrO_4) in water.

$$2\,CrO_4^{2-}(aq,\ yellow) + 2\,H_3O^+(aq) \rightleftharpoons Cr_2O_7^{2-}(aq,\ orange) + 3\,H_2O(l) \qquad \text{(Eq. 4)}$$

You will observe the effects of separately adding sulfuric acid solution (H_2SO_4) and sodium hydroxide solution (NaOH) to the system. An important factor in your study is the fact that hydroxide ion (OH^-) reacts with hydronium ion (H_3O^+) to form water, according to the net ionic equation in Equation 5.

$$OH^-(aq) + H_3O^+(aq) \rightleftharpoons 2\,H_2O(l) \qquad \text{(Eq. 5)}$$

Next, you will study the dissociation equilibrium of acetic acid (CH_3COOH), a weak acid, in water. The dissociation is described in Equation 6.

$$CH_3COOH(aq) + H_2O(l) \rightleftharpoons CH_3COO^-(aq) + H_3O^+(aq) \qquad \text{(Eq. 6)}$$

Because all of the components in this system are colorless, you will add methyl orange indicator to the equilibrium mixture in order to visualize the chemical changes that occur as a result of stress. Methyl orange turns red in the presence of high concentrations of H_3O^+ ion and turns yellow in lower concentrations of H_3O^+ ion. By observing color changes in the equilibrium mixture, you will determine the effect of adding water-soluble sodium acetate trihydrate ($CH_3COONa \cdot 3\,H_2O$) to the equilibrium mixture. Then you will observe the effect of adding NaOH solution to another sample of the equilibrium mixture.

The third equilibrium you will study involves two complex ions formed by the cobalt(II) ion, (Co^{2+}, or cobaltous ion). The net ionic equation for this equilibrium is given in Equation 7. This equilibrium mixture is formed by dissolving cobalt(II) chloride ($CoCl_2$) in water, forming tetrachlorocobalt(II) ion, $[CoCl_4]^{2-}$, which in turn reacts with excess water to form hexaaquo-cobalt(II) ion, $[Co(H_2O)_6]^{2+}$.

$$[CoCl_4]^{2-}(aq,\ blue) + 6\,H_2O(l) \rightleftharpoons [Co(H_2O)_6]^{2+}(aq,\ pink) + 4\,Cl^-(aq) \qquad \text{(Eq. 7)}$$

You will determine the responses of this system at equilibrium to the separate additions of hydrochloric acid solution (HCl) and water.

Finally, you will study the dissolution equilibrium of the salt, ammonium chloride (NH_4Cl) in water, as shown by Equation 8.

$$NH_4Cl(s) \rightleftharpoons NH_4^+(aq) + Cl^-(aq) \qquad \text{(Eq. 8)}$$

Starting with a saturated solution of NH_4Cl at equilibrium, you will determine the effect of the addition of HCl solution and the effects of heating and cooling the mixture.

PROCEDURE

CHEMICAL ALERT

$1M$ acetic acid—corrosive and irritant
ammonium chloride—irritant
saturated ammonium chloride solution—irritant
$0.1M$ cobalt(II) chloride—toxic and irritant
concentrated hydrochloric acid—toxic and corrosive
$0.1\ M$ potassium chromate solution—irritant, oxidant, and suspected carcinogen
and mutagen sodium acetate trihydrate—irritant
$1M$ sodium hydroxide—toxic, corrosive, and irritant
$3M$ sulfuric acid—toxic and corrosive

CAUTION

Wear departmentally approved eye protection while doing this
experiment.

I. Studying the CrO_4^{2-} Ion/ $Cr_2O_7^{2-}$ Ion Equilibrium

NOTE: The numbers appearing in parentheses indicate the specific lines on your
Data Sheet on which the indicated data should be entered.

CAUTION

Potassium chromate is a suspected carcinogen and mutagen, but a
K_2CrO_4 solution can be used safely when handled prudently. Avoid skin contact.
Thoroughly wash your hands with soap or detergent after using the solution. If
you spill any of the solution, immediately notify your laboratory instructor.

1. Measure 3 mL of $0.1M$ K_2CrO_4 solution in a clean, 10-mL graduated
   cylinder and pour the solution into a clean test tube.
   Record the color of the solution on your Data Sheet (1).

CAUTION

$3M$ H_2SO_4 solution is toxic, corrosive, and can cause severe burns.
Prevent contact with your eyes, skin, clothing, and combustible material. Avoid
ingesting the solution. If you spill any solution, immediately notify your laboratory
instructor.

2. Add one drop of $3M$ H_2SO_4 solution to the K_2CrO_4 solution in the test
   tube (Step 1), while stirring with a clean, dry, glass stirring rod.
   Continue adding H_2SO_4 solution dropwise, stirring after each addition,
   until you observe a color change in the equilibrium mixture. Leave the
   stirring rod in the test tube.
   Record your observations on your Data Sheet (2).

CAUTION

1*M* **NaOH solution is toxic, corrosive, and can cause burns. Prevent contact with your eyes, skin, and clothing. Avoid ingesting the solution. If you spill any solution, immediately notify your laboratory instructor.**

3. Add one drop of 1*M* NaOH solution to the equilibrium mixture in the test tube (Step 2), while stirring. Continue adding NaOH solution dropwise, stirring after each addition, until you observe a change in the equilibrium mixture.

   Record your observations on your Data Sheet (3).

4. Label a 150-mL beaker "Discarded Mixtures and Rinses." Pour the equilibrium mixture (Step 3) into the labeled beaker. Rinse the graduated cylinder and the test tube with 3–5 mL of tap water each. Pour the rinses into the labeled beaker. Then rinse the cylinder and test tube twice each with 5 mL of distilled or deionized water. Pour the rinses into the beaker.

5. Transfer the contents of the 150-mL beaker into the container specified by your laboratory instructor and labeled "Discarded Chromate–Dichromate Equilibrium Mixtures." Rinse the beaker with 5 mL of distilled water, and pour the rinse into the same discard container.

NOTE: At this point, your laboratory instructor may ask you to answer Questions 4–8 on your Data Sheet. If not, proceed to Step 6.

II. Studying the Dissociation of CH₃COOH in Water

6. Measure 3 mL of 1*M* CH_3COOH solution in a clean, 10-mL graduated cylinder, and pour into a clean test tube. Add 3 drops of methyl orange indicator solution to the solution in the test tube. Stir the solution with a clean, dry, glass stirring rod.

   Record the color of the initial equilibrium mixture on your Data Sheet (9).

7. Use a micro spatula to add 2 or 3 crystals of CH_3COONa to the test tube (Step 6). Stir the solution until the crystals dissolve. Continue to add individual crystals, stirring after each addition, until you observe a change in the equilibrium mixture. Place the test tube in a clean, 250-mL beaker or a test tube support rack.

   Record your observations on your Data Sheet (10).

8. Measure an additional 3 mL of 1*M* CH_3COOH solution into the 10-mL graduated cylinder, and pour into a second clean test tube. Add 3 drops of methyl orange indicator solution and stir. Add one drop of 1*M* NaOH solution to the second test tube and stir. Continue adding NaOH solution dropwise, stirring after each addition, until you observe a change in the equilibrium mixture.

   Record your observations on your Data Sheet (11).

9. Pour the equilibrium mixtures from both test tubes (Steps 7 and 8) into the 150-mL beaker labeled "Discarded Mixtures and Rinses." Rinse the graduated cylinder and both test tubes with 3–5 mL of tap water each. Pour the rinses into the labeled beaker. Then rinse the cylinder and test tube twice each with 5 mL of distilled water. Pour the rinses into the beaker.

10. Transfer the contents of the 150-mL beaker into the container specified by your laboratory instructor and labeled "Discarded Acetic Acid Equilibrium Mixtures." Rinse the beaker with 5 mL of distilled water, and pour the rinse into the same discard container.

NOTE: At this point, your laboratory instructor may ask you to answer Questions 12–16 on your Data Sheet. If not, proceed to Step 11.

III. Studying the $[CoCl_4]^{2-}$ Ion/$[Co(H_2O)_6]^{2+}$ Ion Equilibrium

11. Prepare a hot-water bath. Pour 100 mL of hot tap water into a 250-mL beaker. Add several boiling stones to the water. Heat the bath on a hot plate so that it will be boiling by the time you are ready to do Step 19.

12. Measure 3 mL of $0.1M$ $CoCl_2$ solution in a clean, 10-mL graduated cylinder, and pour into a clean test tube.
    Record the color of the solution on your Data Sheet (17).

CAUTION   ⚠

Concentrated HCl is toxic, corrosive, and can cause burns. Prevent contact with your eyes, skin, and clothing. Avoid ingesting the substance. If you spill any solution, immediately notify your laboratory instructor.

---

13. Add one drop of concentrated HCl to the test tube (Step 12), while stirring with a clean, dry stirring rod. Continue adding HCl dropwise, stirring after each addition, until you see a change in the equilibrium mixture.
    Record your observations on your Data Sheet (18).
    Continue adding HCl dropwise, stirring after each addition, until no further change occurs.
    Record your observations on your Data Sheet (18).

14. Add distilled water dropwise, to the test tube (Step 13), while stirring, until a change occurs.
    Record your observations on your Data Sheet (19).
    Continue to add distilled water dropwise until no further change occurs.
    Record your observations on your Data Sheet (19).

15. Discard the equilibrium mixture (Step 14) into the 150-mL beaker labeled "Discarded Mixtures and Rinses." Rinse the graduated cylinder and the test tube with 3–5 mL of tap water each. Pour the rinses into the labeled beaker. Then rinse the cylinder and test tube twice each with 5 mL of distilled water. Pour the rinses into the beaker.

16. Transfer the contents of the 150-mL beaker into the container specified by your laboratory instructor and labeled "Discarded Cobalt(II) Ion Equilibrium Mixtures." Rinse the beaker with 5 mL of distilled water and pour the rinse into the same discard container.

NOTE: At this point, your laboratory instructor may ask you to answer Questions 20–24 on your Data Sheet. If not, proceed to Step 17.

IV. Studying the Dissolution of NH₄Cl Equilibrium

17. Measure 3 mL of saturated NH_4Cl solution in a clean, *dry*, 10-mL graduated cylinder, and pour into a clean test tube.

18. Add 1 drop of concentrated HCl to the test tube (Step 17), while stirring. Continue adding concentrated HCl dropwise, stirring after each addition, until you observe a change in the equilibrium mixture.
    Record your observations on your Data Sheet (25).

19. Using a test tube holder, place the test tube and its contents, including the stirring rod, (Step 18) into the boiling water in your hot-water bath. Carefully stir the solution in the test tube while heating for 3 min.
    Record your observations on your Data Sheet (26).
    Turn off the hot plate. Place the test tube in the 250-mL beaker.

20. Use a clean micro spatula to carefully add enough crystals of solid NH_4Cl to cover the bottom of a second clean, dry test tube.

21. Measure 5 mL of distilled water in a clean 10-mL graduated cylinder, and pour onto the solid NH_4Cl in the test tube. Stir the mixture. Feel the test tube to determine if the dissolution of NH_4Cl produces a temperature change.
    Record your observations on your Data Sheet (27).

22. Discard the equilibrium mixtures from the two test tubes (Steps 19 and 21) into the 150-mL beaker labeled "Discarded Mixtures and Rinses." Rinse the graduated cylinder and test tubes with 3–5 mL of tap water each. Pour the rinses into the labeled beaker. Then rinse the cylinder and test tubes twice each with 5 mL of distilled water. Pour the rinses into the labeled beaker.

23. Transfer the contents of the 150-mL beaker into the container specified by your laboratory instructor and labeled "Discarded Ammonium Chloride Equilibrium Mixtures." Rinse the beaker with 5 mL of distilled water, and transfer the rinse into the same discard container.

CAUTION

Wash your hands thoroughly with soap or detergent before leaving the laboratory.

NOTE: If you have not answered all of the questions on your Data Sheet by this point, your laboratory instructor will tell you when you should do so.

Name   Section   Date

Post-Laboratory Questions

(Use the spaces provided for the answers and additional paper if necessary.)

1. A student doing the experiment in this module extended the study of the $[CoCl_4]^{2-}$ ion/$[Co(H_2O)_6]^{2+}$ ion equilibrium. In one test tube, the student added silver nitrate ($AgNO_3$) to a blue equilibrium mixture prepared from $CoCl_2$. The reaction mixture became pink and cloudy, and a white precipitate settled out leaving a clear, pink solution. The student identified the precipitate as silver chloride, $AgCl$.

(1) Briefly explain how these observations are consistent with Le Châtelier's principle.

In a second test, the student placed a test tube containing a pink equilibrium mixture in a hot-water bath. The solution turned blue. When the student removed the test tube from the hot-water bath and placed it in an ice-water bath, the solution turned pink.

(2) Is the forward reaction in the $[CoCl_4]^{2-}$ ion/$[Co(H_2O)_6]^{2+}$ ion equilibrium exothermic or endothermic?

(3) Briefly explain how the student's observations support your answer to (2).

(4) Write the net ionic equation for this equilibrium, including heat.

2. The popular antacid, Milk of Magnesia, is a suspension of magnesium hydroxide, $Mg(OH)_2$. In water, $Mg(OH)_2$ undergoes the reaction shown in Equation 9.

$$Mg(OH)_2(s, \text{ white}) \rightleftharpoons Mg^{2+}(aq) + 2OH^-(aq) \qquad \text{(Eq. 9)}$$

   (1) What would you observe if you added an acid to an equilibrium mixture containing $Mg(OH)_2$ in water?

   (2) Write a chemical equation that accounts for the effect of the added acid.

   (3) Briefly explain how your answer to (1) is consistent with Le Châtelier's principle.

Name   Section   Date

Data Sheet

I. Studying the CrO_4^{2-} Ion/$Cr_2O_7^{2-}$ Ion Equilibrium

(1) What is the color of the solution in Step 1?

(2) What change do you observe when you add H_2SO_4 solution (Step 2)?

(3) What change do you observe when you add NaOH solution (Step 3)?

(4) Write the net ionic equation for the CrO_42- ion/$Cr_2O_7^{2-}$ ion equilibrium.

(5) What, if any, experimental evidence do you have that the equilibrium is affected by the addition of H_2SO_4 solution? Briefly explain.

(6) Are your observation and explanation in (5) consistent with Le Châtelier's principle? Briefly explain.

(7) What, if any, experimental evidence do you have that the equilibrium is affected by the addition of NaOH solution? Briefly explain.

(8) Are your observation and explanation in (7) consistent with Le Châtelier's principle? Briefly explain.

II. Studying the Dissociation of CH₃COOH in Water

(9) What is the color of the initial equilibrium mixture (Step 6)?

(10) What change do you observe when you add solid CH_3COONa (Step 7)?

(11) What change do you observe when you add NaOH solution to the second test tube (Step 8)?

(12) Write the chemical equation for the dissociation of CH_3COOH in water.

(13) What, if any, experimental evidence do you have that the equilibrium is affected by the addition of solid CH_3COONa (Step 7)? Briefly explain.

(14) Are your observation and explanation in (13) consistent with Le Châtelier's principle? Briefly explain.

(15) What, if any, experimental evidence do you have that the equilibrium is affected by the addition of NaOH solution (Step 8)? Briefly explain.

(16) Are your observation and explanation in (15) consistent with Le Châtelier's principle? Briefly explain.

III. Studying the $[CoCl_4]^{2-}$ Ion/$[Co(H_2O)_6]^{2+}$ Ion Equilibrium

(17) What is the color of the solution (Step 12)?

(18) What changes do you observe when you add concentrated HCl (Step 13)?

(19) What change do you observe when you add distilled water (Step 14)?

(20) Write the net ionic equation for the $[CoCl_4]^{2-}$ ion/$[Co(H_2O)_6]^{2+}$ ion equilibrium.

(21) What, if any, experimental evidence do you have that the equilibrium is affected by the addition of concentrated HCl? Briefly explain.

(22) Are your observation and explanation in (21) consistent with Le Châtelier's principle? Briefly explain.

(23) What, if any, experimental evidence do you have that the equilibrium is affected by the addition of distilled H_2O? Briefly explain.

(24) Are your observation and explanation in (23) consistent with Le Châtelier's principle? Briefly explain.

IV. Studying the Dissolution of NH₄Cl Equilibrium

(25) What change do you observe when you add concentrated HCl (Step 18)?

(26) What change do you observe when you heat the equilibrium mixture (Step 19)?

(27) What change do you observe when solid NH_4Cl dissolves in water (Step 21)?

(28) Is the dissolution of NH_4Cl exothermic or endothermic?

(29) Write the chemical equation for the dissolution of NH_4Cl in water.

(30) What, if any, experimental evidence do you have that the equilibrium is affected by the addition of HCl solution? Briefly explain.

(31) Are your observation and explanation in (30) consistent with Le Châtelier's principle? Briefly explain.

(32) What, if any, experimental evidence do you have that the equilibrium is affected by changes in temperature? Briefly explain.

(33) Are your observation and explanation in (32) consistent with Le Châtelier's principle? Briefly explain.

(34) Write the chemical equation for the dissolution of NH_4Cl in water, including heat.

Name   Section   Date

Pre-Laboratory Assignment

1. It is important for you to be aware of the hazards associated with the substances you use in an experiment. These hazards are described throughout the Procedure in the Caution boxes. Briefly describe the hazards associated with the following:

(1) $3M$ H_2SO_4 solution

(2) $0.1M$ K_2CrO_4 solution

(3) concentrated HCl

2. Briefly explain the meanings of the following terms as they relate to this experiment.

(1) forward reaction

(2) reverse reaction

(3) chemical equilibrium

(4) endothermic reaction

3. Iron(III) ion (Fe^{3+}) reacts with thiocyanate ion (SCN^-) to form a red complex ion with the formula $[FeSCN]^{2+}$. The net ionic equation describing this reaction is given in Equation 10.

$$Fe^{3+}(aq, \text{lt. yellow}) + SCN^-(aq, \text{colorless}) \rightleftharpoons [FeSCN]^{2+}(aq, \text{red}) \qquad \text{(Eq. 10)}$$

A student studying this equilibrium begins with an equilibrium mixture that is light pink.

(1) What change will the student observe when a solution containing Fe^{3+} ion is added to this mixture?

(2) Briefly explain how your answer to (1) is consistent with Le Châtelier's principle.

(3) Silver ion (Ag^+) reacts with SCN^- ion to form silver thiocyanate (AgSCN). What change will the student observe when a solution containing Ag^+ ion is added to the mixture?

(4) Briefly explain how your answer to (3) is consistent with Le Châtelier's principle.

Monitoring Acid–Base Titrations with a pH Meter

Prepared by John W. Alcock, Quinnipiac College, and
M. L. Gillette, Indiana University Kokomo

PURPOSE OF THE EXPERIMENT

Use a pH meter to record titrant solution pH data. Collect titrant volume for titrations of hydrochloric acid and of acetic acid with standardized sodium hydroxide solution. Prepare titration curves from the collected data. Calculate hydronium and hydroxide ion concentrations at various points throughout the titrations. Use the titration curves and calculations to compare the behavior of the two acids.

BACKGROUND INFORMATION

Analysts frequently determine the acid content of solutions such as rainwater and industrial wastes. To do this, they take advantage of neutralization reactions between acids and bases. One such example is the neutralization of hydrochloric acid solution (HCl) with the base sodium hydroxide (NaOH), shown in Equation 1.

$$HCl(aq) + NaOH(aq) \rightarrow H_2O(l) + NaCl(aq) \qquad (Eq.\ 1)$$

We can carry out the neutralization quantitatively by titration. **Titration** is the addition of a chemically equivalent volume of a solution of known concentration, called a **standardized solution**, to the solution of unknown concentration being analyzed. We add the standardized solution, the **titrant**, from a buret to accurately measure the volume required for the neutralization. When the solution being analyzed is acidic, it is convenient to use a standardized NaOH solution as the titrant.

I. Titrating a Strong Acid with a Strong Base

We classify acids as strong or weak depending upon their extent of dissociation in water. When dissolved in water, virtually every molecule of a **strong acid** dissociates, releasing a hydrogen ion (H^+) to a water molecule, producing a hydronium ion (H_3O^+). Equation 2 shows the reaction of HCl, a strong acid, in water.

$$HCl(aq) + H_2O(l) \rightarrow H_3O^+(aq) + Cl^-(aq) \qquad \text{(Eq. 2)}$$

Sodium hydroxide is a water-soluble ionic compound that completely dissociates into sodium ions (Na^+) and hydroxide ions (OH^-). Hence, NaOH is a strong base. We can more accurately represent the neutralization reaction of HCl with an NaOH solution in the complete ionic equation shown in Equation 3.

$$H_3O^+(aq) + Cl^-(aq) + Na^+(aq) + OH^-(aq) \rightarrow 2\,H_2O(l) + Na^+(aq) + Cl^-(aq) \qquad \text{(Eq. 3)}$$

Sodium ions and chloride ions (Cl^-) are **spectator ions** in this reaction, appearing unchanged as both reactants and products. Therefore, we can cancel them from Equation 3 to create the net ionic equation, Equation 4.

$$H_3O^+(aq) + OH^-(aq) \rightleftharpoons 2\,H_2O(l) \qquad \text{(Eq. 4)}$$

We can monitor any acid–base titration by following changes in H_3O^+ concentration in solution. This is convenient, because H_3O^+ concentration is related to the **pH** of the solution as defined by Equation 5. Note that the square brackets represent the molarity (M, mol/L) of H_3O^+.

$$pH = -\log[H_3O^+] \qquad \text{(Eq. 5)}$$

We monitor pH during a titration using a pH meter equipped with an electrode responsive to H_3O^+ concentration in solution.

Initially, the pH of the HCl solution will be low, because there are as many moles of H_3O^+ present as there are moles of HCl. As we add NaOH solution, the reaction in Equation 4 occurs, decreasing $[H_3O^+]$. This causes a corresponding increase in solution pH.

This neutralization reaction is complete at the **equivalence point**, when the number of moles of OH^- added as titrant equals the number of moles of H_3O^+ originally present in solution. The pH at the equivalence point is established by the components of the titration mixture. For the titration of HCl with NaOH, a strong acid with a strong base, Equation 3 shows that the only species present at the equivalence point are Na^+, Cl^-, and H_2O. Because neither Na^+ nor Cl^- react with water (and are, therefore, neutral ions), the pH of the titration mixture at the equivalence point is established by the dissociation of water, shown in Equation 6.

$$2\,H_2O(l) \rightleftharpoons H_3O^+(aq) + OH^-(aq) \qquad \text{(Eq. 6)}$$

The equilibrium constant expression representing this reaction is shown in Equation 7. At 25 °C, the dissociation constant for water is 1.0×10^{-14}.

$$K_w = [H_3O^+][OH^-] = 1.0 \times 10^{-14} \qquad \text{(Eq. 7)}$$

At the equivalence point of our NaOH and HCl titration, H_3O^+ and OH^- concentrations are equal (Equation 6). Therefore, $[H_3O^+] = (1.0 \times 10^{-14})^{1/2} = 1 \times 10^{-7} M$, and the pH of the solution is 7 (Equation 5).

If we continue to add NaOH solution to the titration mixture after the equivalence point, the pH will continue to increase.

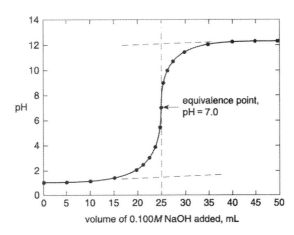

Figure 1
A typical titration curve for a strong acid with 0.100M NaOH

If we plot the pH of a titration mixture versus volume of titrant added, we obtain a graph called a **titration curve**. Figure 1 shows a typical curve for the titration of a strong acid with NaOH solution. We can locate the equivalence point of the titration by drawing a vertical line through the midpoint of the steep portion of the curve. The titrant volume and pH of the solution at the equivalence point correspond to the x and y coordinates, respectively, of the point where the vertical line intersects the titration curve.

II. Titrating a Weak Acid with a Strong Base

Most acids are weak. When a **weak acid** is dissolved in water, only a small percent of the acid molecules dissociate to produce H_3O^+. Acetic acid ($HC_2H_3O_2$), the pungent component of vinegar, is a typical weak acid. We can represent its dissociation in water by Equation 8.

$$HC_2H_3O_2(aq) + H_2O(l) \rightleftharpoons H_3O^+(aq) + C_2H_3O_2^-(aq) \qquad \text{(Eq. 8)}$$

The equilibrium constant expression for the dissociation of $HC_2H_3O_2$ is shown in Equation 9. The dissociation constant for $HC_2H_3O_2$ at 25 °C is 1.8×10^{-5}.

$$K_a = \frac{[H_3O^+][C_2H_3O_2^-]}{[HC_2H_3O_2]} = 1.8 \times 10^5 \qquad \text{(Eq. 9)}$$

The pH of an $HC_2H_3O_2$ solution is higher than that of an HCl solution of equal concentration, because only about 5% of the $HC_2H_3O_2$ molecules dissociate, whereas essentially all of the HCl molecules do so.

If we titrate an $HC_2H_3O_2$ solution with NaOH solution, the reaction shown in Equation 10 occurs.

$$HC_2H_3O_2(aq) + NaOH(aq) \rightarrow NaC_2H_3O_2(aq) + H_2O(l) \qquad \text{(Eq. 10)}$$

The complete ionic equation (Equation 11) and net ionic equation (Equation 12) for this reaction are shown below.

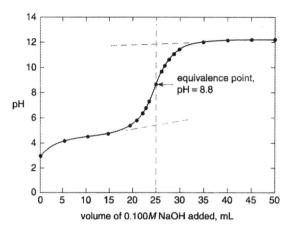

Figure 2
A typical titration curve for a weak acid with 0.100M NaOH

$$HC_2H_3O_2(aq) + Na^+(aq) + OH^-(aq) \rightarrow Na^+(aq) + C_2H_3O_2^-(aq) + H_2O(l) \qquad \text{(Eq. 11)}$$

$$HC_2H_3O_2(aq) + OH^-(aq) \rightarrow C_2H_3O_2^-(aq) + H_2O(l) \qquad \text{(Eq. 12)}$$

As we add NaOH solution to the $HC_2H_3O_2$ solution, $HC_2H_3O_2$ is converted into acetate ions ($C_2H_3O_2^-$). The solution pH depends upon the relative concentrations of these two species (Equation 9). As with the titration of HCl solution with NaOH solution, the pH of the $HC_2H_3O_2$–NaOH titration mixture at the equivalence point is established by the components present at that point: $C_2H_3O_2^-$, Na^+, and H_2O.

Sodium ions are neutral in terms of pH, so they do not play a role in pH. However, because $C_2H_3O_2^-$ ions are the anions of a weak acid, they react with H_2O, or **hydrolyze**, as shown in Equation 13.

$$C_2H_3O_2^-(aq) + H_2O(l) \rightleftharpoons HC_2H_3O_2(aq) + OH^-(aq) \qquad \text{(Eq. 13)}$$

The equilibrium constant expression, K_h, at 25 °C for the hydrolysis reaction is shown in Equation 14.

$$K_h = \frac{[OH^-]\,[HC_2H_3O_2]}{[C_2H_3O_2^-]} = 5.6 \times 10^{10} \qquad \text{(Eq. 14)}$$

The other equilibrium that could occur at this equivalence point is the dissociation of water, shown in Equation 6. Because K_h is larger than K_w, the hydrolysis reaction takes precedence. Therefore, the pH of the reaction mixture at the equivalence point is greater than 7.0, due to the presence of OH^- produced by the hydrolysis of $C_2H_3O_2^-$.

A typical titration curve for the titration of a weak acid with 0.100M NaOH is shown in Figure 2.

III. Calculating H₃O⁺ and OH⁻ Concentrations for Points on a Titration Curve

We can calculate the molarity of H_3O^+ and OH^- from the pH at any point on a titration curve. Suppose we find from our titration curve that the solution pH is 4.60 when we have added 10.0 mL of 0.100M NaOH to 25.0 mL of an $HC_2H_3O_2$ solution. To determine $[H_3O^+]$ and $[OH^-]$ for the mixture at this point, we substitute 4.60 into Equation 5, and solve for $[H_3O^+]$.

$$4.60 = -\log[H_3O^+]$$

$$-4.60 = \log[H_3O^+]$$

$$[H_3O^+] = \text{antilog}{-4.60} = 2.5 \times 10^{-5} M$$

Using Equation 7, we can calculate $[OH^-]$.

$$[OH^-] = \frac{1.0 \times 10^{-14}}{2.5 \times 10^{-5}} = 4.0 \times 10^{-10} M$$

Using the same process, we can calculate $[H_3O^+]$ and $[OH^-]$ for any point on the titration curve.

PROCEDURE

Preview

- Calibrate a pH meter
- Fill buret with standardized NaOH solution
- Titrate HCl solution with standardized NaOH solution, monitoring the reaction mixture pH as titrant added
- Titrate $HC_2H_3O_2$ solution with standardized NaOH solution, monitoring reaction mixture pH as titrant added

CHEMICAL ALERT

0.100*M* **acetic acid—irritant**
0.100*M* **hydrochloric acid—toxic and corrosive**
0.100*M* **sodium hydroxide—toxic and corrosive**

CAUTION

Wear departmentally approved safety goggles while doing this experiment.

I. Calibrating the pH Meter

CAUTION

Glass electrodes are fragile and expensive. Do not bump the glass membrane against anything solid.

NOTE: Your laboratory instructor will describe and demonstrate a satisfactory method for calibrating the pH meters available in your laboratory. Depending upon the model of pH meters available, you will perform this calibration using either one or two buffer solutions.

Consult your laboratory instructor to make sure your electrode is properly vented.

Transfer 50 mL of the designated buffer solution into a 150-mL beaker. Carefully immerse the electrode(s) in the solution.

Turn the function knob to "pH" or, on some instruments, "read". Turn the standardize knob until the meter indicates the exact pH of the buffer solution. Do not turn this knob again during the course of the Procedure. Turn the function knob to "standby".

On Data Sheet 1, record the pH(s) at which you standardized the meter.

II. Titrating HCl Solution with NaOH Solution

CAUTION

0.100*M* HCl and 0.100*M* NaOH are toxic and corrosive. Prevent eye, skin, and clothing contact.

Obtain 25.00 mL of an approximately 0.100*M* HCl solution in a clean, 250-mL beaker. Also obtain 125 mL of an approximately 0.100*M* NaOH solution in a clean, dry 250-mL Erlenmeyer flask. Record the exact molarity of each solution on Data Sheet 1.

Rinse a clean 50-mL buret with three separate 10-mL portions of distilled water. With the stopcock closed, hold the buret in a nearly horizontal position, and slowly rotate it so that the water contacts the entire inner surface of the buret. Drain the rinse water through the buret tip into the sink. Following the same procedure, rinse the buret with three 5-mL portions of your NaOH solution. Drain the NaOH solution into a beaker labeled "Discarded NaOH Solution".

Clamp the buret to a support stand. Fill the buret with your NaOH solution to a point above the top calibration mark. Drain the solution through the buret tip into the "Discarded NaOH Solution" beaker until the meniscus is at a point within the calibrated portion of the buret. The meniscus does not have to be exactly at the 0.00-mL mark. Remove any air bubbles in the buret tip. Read the initial solution volume to the nearest 0.02 mL, and record it on Data Sheet 1.

NOTE: Your laboratory instructor may tell you to stir your titration mixture with a magnetic stirrer and stir bar. If so, be certain to position the electrode so that the stir bar will not hit the glass membrane.

Position the beaker containing the HCl solution so that the glass membrane of the electrode is immersed in the solution. Position the buret containing NaOH solution just inside the beaker, with the tip below the rim but above the solution surface, as shown in Figure 3. Ask your laboratory instructor to check your equipment setup.

Adjust the function knob of your pH meter from "standby" to "pH", or "read".

While stirring the HCl solution continuously, begin slowly adding 1- or 2-mL portions of NaOH solution. After each addition, record the pH and the corresponding buret reading on Data Sheet 1.

When successive pH readings begin to increase rapidly, add NaOH solution dropwise until successive pH readings are increasing only slightly. When you reach this stage, begin gradually increasing the amount of titrant you add each time. Stop adding NaOH solution when the pH reaches 11.5.

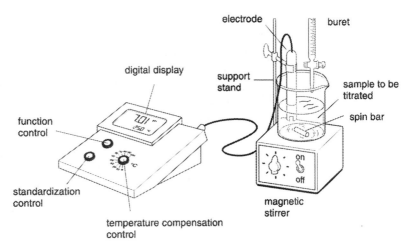

Figure 3
A pH meter–titration apparatus

NOTE: If you are using a magnetic stirrer, do not let the stir bar fall into the drain during the next step.

After the titration is complete, leave the electrode in place. Add 0.100*M* HCl solution to reduce the titration mixture pH to between 4 and 8. Pour the titration mixture into the drain, diluting with a large amount of running water.

Repeat the above procedure with a second 25.00-mL sample of 0.100*M* HCl. Record all data on Data Sheet 1.

III. Titrating HC$_2$H$_3$O$_2$ Solution with NaOH Solution

CAUTION

0.100*M* HC$_2$H$_3$O$_2$ is an irritant. Prevent eye, skin, and clothing contact.

Follow the Procedure in Part II, using 25.00 mL of approximately 0.100*M* HC$_2$H$_3$O$_2$ in place of the 0.100*M* HCl. Record the exact molarity of the HC$_2$H$_3$O$_2$ solution and all titration data on Data Sheet 1.

CAUTION

0.100*M* HCl is a toxic, corrosive solution that can cause severe burns.
Prevent eye, skin, and clothing contact. Avoid inhaling the vapors or ingesting the compound. If you spill any acid, immediately notify your laboratory instructor.

NOTE: If you are using a magnetic stirrer, do not let the stir bar fall into the drain during the next step.

After completing the titrations in Parts II and III, transfer the NaOH solution in the buret and the flask into the "Discarded NaOH Solution" beaker. Insert the electrode(s) and stir bar, if you are using one, into the NaOH solution. Add 0.100*M* HCl dropwise until the solution pH is between

4 and 8. Pour the solution into the drain, diluting with a large amount of running water.

Rinse your buret twice using 10-mL portions of tap water, then twice using 10-mL of distilled water. Drain the buret. With the stopcock open, clamp the buret to the support stand in an inverted position, so it can drain. Rinse the electrode with distilled water. Immerse the electrode tip in pH 7 buffer solution.

CAUTION

Wash your hands thoroughly with soap or detergent before leaving the laboratory.

CALCULATIONS

Do the following calculations, and record the results on the graph paper supplied and Data Sheet 2.

II. Titrating HCl Solution with NaOH Solution

1. Prepare a titration curve. Plot pH (on the y-axis) versus volume of NaOH solution added (on the x-axis). If your initial buret reading was not 0.00 mL, remember to subtract your actual initial reading from each of your subsequent buret readings before plotting the titration data.

III. Titrating $HC_2H_3O_2$ Solution with NaOH Solution

2. On a separate piece of graph paper, prepare a titration curve from your data for Part III.

3. Using your titration curves and Equations 5 and 7, calculate $[H_3O^+]$ and $[OH^-]$ in the reaction mixture at the following points in each titration:

   (1) before you added any NaOH solution

   (2) after you added 10.00 mL of NaOH solution

   (3) before you added the 0.20 mL of NaOH solution needed to reach the equivalence point

   (4) at the equivalence point

   (5) after you added 0.20 mL of NaOH solution past the equivalence point

   (6) after you added the last portion of NaOH solution

Name   _Section_   _Date_

Post-Laboratory Questions

(Use the spaces provided for the answers and additional paper if necessary.)

1. Briefly explain why the part of the curve beyond the equivalence point is similar in the graphs from Parts II and III, even though you titrated a strong acid in Part II and a weak acid in Part III.

2. A student began his Part II titration with an air bubble in the buret tip. The bubble was released, unnoticed, at some point during the titration. Briefly describe the error that the bubble would have caused in his titration results if:

(a) the bubble had been released prior to the equivalence point of the titration.

(b) the bubble had been released after the equivalence point.

3. (a) Briefly outline a procedure you could use to determine the $HC_2H_3O_2$ concentration in a vinegar sample.

(b) Make a rough sketch of the shape of the titration curve for the determination in (a).

(c) What would the pH be at the equivalence point of the titration? Briefly explain.

4. (a) Sketch an approximate titration curve for the titration of an NaOH solution with standardized HCl solution. Briefly explain the shape of the curve before the equivalence point, at the equivalence point, and after the equivalence point.

(b) What would the pH be at the equivalence point of the titration in (a)? Briefly explain.

_____   _____   _____
Name   *Section*   *Date*

Data Sheet 1

pH(s) at which meter was standardized: _____   _____

II. Titrating HCl Solution with NaOH Solution

concentration of HCl solution, M _____

concentration of NaOH solution, M _____

_____

| | *first determination* | | | *second determination* | |
| | | | | | |

initial buret reading, mL _____   initial buret reading, mL _____

pH	*buret reading, mL*	*volume NaOH added, mL*	pH	*buret reading, mL*	*volume NaOH added, mL*
____	____	____	____	____	____
____	____	____	____	____	____
____	____	____	____	____	____
____	____	____	____	____	____
____	____	____	____	____	____
____	____	____	____	____	____
____	____	____	____	____	____
____	____	____	____	____	____
____	____	____	____	____	____
____	____	____	____	____	____
____	____	____	____	____	____
____	____	____	____	____	____
____	____	____	____	____	____
____	____	____	____	____	____

III. Titrating HC₂H₃O₂ Solution with NaOH Solution

concentration of NaOH solution, M _____

concentration of HC₂H₃O₂ solution, M _____

first determination			*second determination*		
initial buret reading, mL _____			initial buret reading, mL _____		
pH	*buret reading, mL*	*volume NaOH added, mL*	pH	*buret reading, mL*	*volume NaOH added, mL*
_____	_____	_____	_____	_____	_____
_____	_____	_____	_____	_____	_____
_____	_____	_____	_____	_____	_____
_____	_____	_____	_____	_____	_____
_____	_____	_____	_____	_____	_____
_____	_____	_____	_____	_____	_____
_____	_____	_____	_____	_____	_____
_____	_____	_____	_____	_____	_____
_____	_____	_____	_____	_____	_____
_____	_____	_____	_____	_____	_____
_____	_____	_____	_____	_____	_____
_____	_____	_____	_____	_____	_____
_____	_____	_____	_____	_____	_____
_____	_____	_____	_____	_____	_____
_____	_____	_____	_____	_____	_____
_____	_____	_____	_____	_____	_____

Name _____   *Section* _____   *Date* _____

Data Sheet 2

II. Titrating HCl Solution with NaOH Solution

	first determination			second determination		
	pH	$[H_3O^+]$	$[OH^-]$	*pH*	$[H_3O^+]$	$[OH^-]$
(1) before adding NaOH solution	_____	_____	_____	_____	_____	_____
(2) after adding 10.00 mL	_____	_____	_____	_____	_____	_____
(3) 0.20 mL before equivalence point	_____	_____	_____	_____	_____	_____
(4) at equivalence point	_____	_____	_____	_____	_____	_____
(5) 0.20 mL past equivalence point	_____	_____	_____	_____	_____	_____
(6) after last addition	_____	_____	_____	_____	_____	_____

III. Titrating HC$_2$H$_3$O$_2$ Solution with NaOH Solution

	first determination			second determination		
	pH	$[H_3O^+]$	$[OH^-]$	*pH*	$[H_3O^+]$	$[OH^-]$
(1) before adding NaOH solution	_____	_____	_____	_____	_____	_____
(2) after adding 10.00 mL	_____	_____	_____	_____	_____	_____
(3) 0.20 mL before equivalence point	_____	_____	_____	_____	_____	_____
(4) at equivalence point	_____	_____	_____	_____	_____	_____
(5) 0.20 mL past equivalence point	_____	_____	_____	_____	_____	_____
(6) after last addition	_____	_____	_____	_____	_____	_____

Name _____   Section _____   Date _____

Pre-Laboratory Assignment

1. Briefly explain:

    (a) why you must use caution when working with HCl solutions.

    (b) what you will do with the NaOH solution remaining in your buret after you have completed your titrations.

2. Calculate $[H_3O^+]$ and $[OH^-]$ in solutions of

	$[H_3O^+] =$	$[OH^-] =$
(a) pH 4.18	_____	_____
(b) pH 5.70	_____	_____
(c) pH 8.56	_____	_____

3. A student titrated 20.0 mL of 0.410M HCl with 0.320M NaOH and collected the following data.

volume NaOH solution added, mL	pH
0.00	0.39
2.00	0.46
4.00	0.54
6.00	0.62
8.00	0.70
10.00	0.78
12.00	0.87
14.00	0.96
16.00	1.07
18.00	1.19
20.00	1.35
22.00	1.56
24.00	1.93
24.50	2.09
25.00	2.35
25.50	3.06
26.00	11.40
26.50	11.80
27.00	12.00
28.00	12.20
29.00	12.30

(a) Prepare a titration curve for this titration.

(b) Identify the volume of titrant required to reach the equivalence point of the titration.

(c) What are the pH, $[H_3O^+]$, and $[OH^-]$ when 21.50 mL of titrant has been added?

Studying the Rate of the Reaction of Potassium Permanganate and Oxalic Acid

Prepared by Richard C. Bell, Lebanon Valley College,
and M. L. Gillette, Indiana University Kokomo

PURPOSE OF THE EXPERIMENT

Determine the order with respect to permanganate ion and to oxalic acid concentrations for the reaction of potassium permanganate and oxalic acid solutions. Write a rate equation for this reaction. Determine the effect of increased temperature on the rate of this reaction.

BACKGROUND INFORMATION

In chemical reactions, reactant ions or molecules must collide with sufficient energy and proper orientation before their transition to product species can occur. We can learn a great deal about which collisions are most significant from a study of factors that enhance the **rate**, or velocity, with which the reaction proceeds. **Kinetics** is the study of reaction rates and of the mechanisms, or bond breaking and bond making processes, by which chemical reactions occur.

The relative proportions of reactant and product species engaging in any reaction are governed by the stoichiometry of the reaction. Therefore, the rate at which any reactant concentration decreases in the reaction mixture is proportional to the rate at which any product concentration increases. Thus, we can measure reaction rates by measuring the decrease of any reactant concentration or the increase in any product concentration. Our choice is one of convenience. For example, if only one reactant is colored, we can visually or instrumentally observe its initial presence, as well as its disappearance as the reactant is consumed in the reaction. If one reactant and one product are differently colored, we can watch the reaction mixture change color as the colored reactant disappears and the product concentration increases.

The Effect of Reactant Concentrations on Reaction Rate

Because reactions require collisions of reactant species, reaction rates often increase when the collision frequency and/or the collision energy of the reactants increases. We can increase this collision frequency in several ways. First, we can increase the reactant concentrations in the mixture. In chemical reactions involving more than one reactant, the reaction rate is often differently affected by a concentration increase of one compared to another of the reactants.

We describe the effect of such concentration increases on the reaction rate by writing the rate equation for the reaction. A **rate equation** shows the mathematical relationship between the individual reactant concentrations and the reaction rate. The relationship between an increase in a reactant concentration and the reaction rate increase (or decrease) is expressed as an exponential term called the **reaction order** with respect to that reactant. The rate equation for the reaction shown in Equation 1 takes the general form shown in Equation 2. In Equation 2, [A] and [B] represent the molar concentrations (mol/L) of A and B, x is the reaction order with respect to reactant A, y is the reaction order with respect to reactant B, and k is the **rate constant**, a proportionality constant that varies only when the reaction temperature changes.

$$A + B \rightarrow C + D \tag{Eq. 1}$$

$$\text{rate} = k[A]^x[B]^y \tag{Eq. 2}$$

The **overall reaction order** is the sum of the orders of the individual reactants, $x + y$ in this case. Reaction orders are usually small positive or negative whole numbers (e.g., 1, 2, -1) or fractions (e.g., $1/2$, $-1/2$).

A. Identifying the Order of a Reaction

If a reaction rate doubles when the concentration of one reactant is doubled, the reaction rate is directly proportional to that reactant concentration. The reaction order with respect to that reactant is one, and we say that the reaction is **first order** with respect to that reactant.

Consider, for example, the reaction of nitrogen(IV) oxide (NO_2) and hydrogen chloride (HCl), shown in Equation 3.

$$NO_2(g) + 2\,HCl(g) \rightarrow NO(g) + H_2O(g) + Cl_2(g) \tag{Eq. 3}$$

From experimental data, we find that the rate of this reaction is directly proportional to the NO_2 concentration. Therefore, this reaction is first order with respect to NO_2. We also find that the reaction rate is doubled when only the HCl concentration is doubled. Hence, the reaction is also first order with respect to HCl. The rate equation for this reaction is shown in Equation 4.

$$\text{rate} = k[NO_2][HCl] \tag{Eq. 4}$$

The overall reaction order of this reaction is two, so we say that, overall, this is a **second order reaction**.

A reaction can also be second order with respect to the concentration of a single reactant. If a reaction rate is squared as the result of doubling the concentration of one of the reactants, the reaction is second order with respect to that reactant. For example, the decomposition of NO_2 at an elevated temperature, shown in Equation 5, has been experimentally found to be second order with respect to NO_2.

$$2\, NO_2(g) \rightarrow 2\, NO(g) + O_2(g) \qquad \text{(Eq. 5)}$$

The rate equation for this reaction is given in Equation 6.

$$\text{rate} = k[NO_2]^2 \qquad \text{(Eq. 6)}$$

We must determine the rate equation for any chemical reaction experimentally. Occasionally, the exponents of the rate equation coincide with the reactant coefficients in the balanced chemical equation, but when this happens it is a coincidence.

B. Determining the Rate Equation for a Reaction from Experimental Data

How can we use laboratory data to determine the rate equation for a reaction? Consider the reaction of sulfur(IV) oxide (SO_2) and hydrogen (H_2), shown in Equation 7.

$$SO_2(g) + 2\, H_2(g) \rightarrow S(s) + 2\, H_2O(g) \qquad \text{(Eq. 7)}$$

The rate equation for this reaction takes the general form shown in Equation 8.

$$\text{rate} = k[SO_2]^x[H_2]^y \qquad \text{(Eq. 8)}$$

We can determine the reaction order with respect to SO_2 (x) and to H_2 (y) using the **method of initial rates**. This method involves measuring and comparing the initial reaction rates when the initial reactant concentrations are independently changed. For example, consider the three determinations described in Table 1. The rate equations for these determinations are shown as Equations 9–11.

$$\text{rate}_1 = k[SO_2]_1^x[H_2]_1^y \qquad \text{(Eq. 9)}$$

$$\text{rate}_2 = k[SO_2]_2^x[H_2]_2^y \qquad \text{(Eq. 10)}$$

$$\text{rate}_3 = k[SO_2]_3^x[H_2]_3^y \qquad \text{(Eq. 11)}$$

Note that, because the reactions were run at constant temperature, the rate constant for each determination is the same. Rate data from these three determinations are shown in Table 1.

From a comparison of the results of determinations 1 and 2, we can establish the effect on the reaction rate of doubling the initial SO_2 concentration, because the H_2 concentration was held constant. We can also determine x in the rate equation by comparing the rates obtained in determinations 1 and 2. Similarly, we can compare the results of determinations 2 and 3 to determine the effect of doubling the initial H_2 concentration on the reaction rate.

Table 1 *The reaction rate of SO_2 with H_2 at constant temperature and different initial reactant concentrations*

Determination number	Initial concentration of SO_2, mol/L	Concentration of H_2, mol/L	Reaction rate, mol/L $\cdot$ s
1	1.50×10^{-3}	3.00×10^{-3}	4.95×10^{-7}
2	3.00×10^{-3}	3.00×10^{-3}	9.90×10^{-7}
3	3.00×10^{-3}	1.50×10^{-3}	4.95×10^{-7}

As we can see from determinations 1 and 2, the rate doubles when the initial SO_2 concentration is doubled. Because the rate is directly proportional to the SO_2 concentration, we say that the reaction is first order with respect to SO_2, and that $x = 1$. We can show this mathematically as follows. Dividing Equation 10 by Equation 9 allows us to cancel the rate constant and gives the ratios:

$$\left(\frac{\text{rate}_2}{\text{rate}_1} \right) = \left(\frac{[SO_2]_2^{\,x}\,[H_2]_2^{\,y}}{[SO_2]_1^{\,x}\,[H_2]_1^{\,y}} \right)$$

Because the $[H_2]$ was the same in determinations 1 and 2, we can cancel the two $[H_2]$ terms and simplify the ratio:

$$\left(\frac{\text{rate}_2}{\text{rate}_1} \right) = \left(\frac{[SO_2]_2^{\,x}}{[SO_2]_1^{\,x}} \right)$$

Substituting the data from Table 1 into the simplified ratio gives:

$$\frac{9.90 \times 10^{-7}\,\text{mol/L} \cdot \text{s}}{4.95 \times 10^{-7}\,\text{mol/L} \cdot \text{s}} = \frac{(3.00 \times 10^{-3}\,\text{mol/L})^x}{(1.50 \times 10^{-3}\,\text{mol/L})^x}$$

Dividing the numerators by the denominators results in:

$$2.00 = 2.00^x$$

Solving for x, we find:

$$x = 1$$

In similar fashion, we can use the data from determinations 2 and 3 to establish that $y = 1$. Therefore, the reaction is also first order with respect to H_2. Finally, we can determine that the reaction is second order overall ($x + y = 1 + 1 = 2$).

Having established the exponents for both SO_2 and H_2, we can write the rate equation for the reaction in Equation 7, as shown in Equation 12. Note that when an exponent is 1, we do not need to write it, because any number raised to the first power is equal to the number itself.

$$\text{rate} = k[SO_2][H_2] \qquad \qquad \text{(Eq. 12)}$$

We can determine the rate constant, k, by substituting the experimental rate and initial concentrations from any determination into Equation 12. For example, substituting the data from determination 1 into Equation 12, we can calculate k.

$$4.95 \times 10^{-7} \ \text{mol/L} \cdot \text{s} = k(1.50 \times 10^{-3} \ \text{mol/L})(3.00 \times 10^{-3} \ \text{mol/L})$$

Or,

$$k = \frac{4.95 \times 10^{-7} \ \text{mol/L} \cdot \text{s}}{(1.50 \times 10^{-3} \ \text{mol/L})(3.00 \times 10^{-3} \ \text{mol/L})} = 0.110 \ \text{L/mol} \cdot \text{s}$$

We can now write the complete rate equation for the reaction in Equation 7 as shown in Equation 13.

$$\text{rate} = (0.110 \ \text{L/mol} \cdot \text{s})[SO_2][H_2] \qquad \text{(Eq. 13)}$$

The Effect of Reaction Temperature on Reaction Rate

Molecular velocity is proportional to temperature. Thus, by increasing the reactant temperatures, we can increase the velocity of the colliding species, and hence, the energy of reactant collisions. Frequently, such an increase results in an increased reaction rate. There is a rule of thumb that, for many reactions, the reaction rate doubles with every 10-degree increase in reactant temperature. To test this generalization, we can establish the effect of temperature on the rate of a reaction. The test includes a series of rate determinations in which we vary the reaction temperature but not the initial reactant concentrations.

In this experiment, you will investigate the rate of the reaction between solutions of potassium permanganate ($KMnO_4$) and oxalic acid ($H_2C_2O_4$), using the method of initial rates. The chemistry of this reaction is very complex. For the purposes of this investigation, you may assume that the sequence of color changes from purple to red to yellow signals the end of the reaction and indicates that the $KMnO_4$ has completely reacted. You may also assume that the general rate equation for this reaction is as shown in Equation 14.

$$\text{rate} = k[H_2C_2O_4]^x[KMnO_4]^y \qquad \text{(Eq. 14)}$$

To establish the reaction rate, you will measure the time that elapses between the mixing of reactants and the disappearance of $KMnO_4$. Then, you will calculate the reaction rate using Equation 15, where $\Delta[KMnO_4]$ is the difference between the initial $[KMnO_4]$ and the $[KMnO_4]$ after the reaction takes place, and Δt is the elapsed time.

$$\text{rate} = -\Delta[KMnO_4]/\Delta t \qquad \text{(Eq. 15)}$$

You will individually vary the initial $H_2C_2O_4$ and $KMnO_4$ concentrations to establish the effect such changes have on the observed reaction rate. From these data, you will propose a rate equation for this reaction. You will also perform the reaction at several temperatures to determine the effect of temperature on the reaction rate.

In each determination you do, you will mix distilled or deionized water with $KMnO_4$ and $H_2C_2O_4$ solutions of predetermined concentrations. Thus, you will dilute the $KMnO_4$ and $H_2C_2O_4$ solutions from their original concentrations. Therefore, you will have to calculate the initial concentrations of these reagents at the beginning of each reaction.

PROCEDURE

Preview

- Rinse, label, and fill three burets, one each with distilled or deionized water, 0.755M $H_2C_2O_4$, and 0.130M $KMnO_4$.
- Time reactions of $KMnO_4$ and $H_2C_2O_4$ using the various solution volumes given in Table 2.
- Time reactions of $KMnO_4$ and $H_2C_2O_4$ solutions after heating the solutions to the various temperatures.

Chemical Alert

0.755M oxalic acid—toxic and corrosive

0.130M potassium permanganate—corrosive and oxidant

CAUTION

Wear departmentally approved safety goggles while doing this experiment.

I. Preparing to Measure Solution Volumes

NOTE: Your laboratory instructor will describe and demonstrate a satisfactory method for cleaning, rinsing, filling, delivering liquids from, and reading a buret.

1. Attach a clean, 50-mL buret to a buret clamp, and label it "Water". Fill the buret with distilled or deionized water.

CAUTION

Oxalic acid ($H_2C_2O_4$) is toxic and corrosive. Prevent eye, skin, and clothing contact. In case of a spill, immediately notify your laboratory instructor.

2. Obtain 60 mL of 0.755M $H_2C_2O_4$ in a labeled 100-mL beaker.
3. Attach a clean 50-mL buret to a buret clamp, label it "$H_2C_2O_4$", and rinse it with a 5-mL portion of the $H_2C_2O_4$ solution. Allow the rinsings to run through the buret tip into a 250-mL beaker labeled "Discarded $H_2C_2O_4$ Solution".

   Fill the buret with $H_2C_2O_4$. Record the *exact* concentration of the $H_2C_2O_4$ solution on Data Sheet 1.

NOTE: Your laboratory instructor will explain how you will obtain the $KMnO_4$ solution necessary for this experiment.

4. Record the *exact* concentration of the $KMnO_4$ solution you will use in this experiment on Data Sheet 1.

Table 2 *Reagent proportions for determinations 1, 2, and 3*

	Determination		
Reactants	*1*	*2*	*3*
$H_2C_2O_4$ solution, mL	5.00	10.00	5.00
$KMnO_4$ solution, mL	1.00	1.00	2.00
Distilled water, mL	6.00	1.00	5.00

5. Record the room temperature, measured to the nearest degree, on Data Sheet 1.

6. Assemble six clean, dry 20 × 150-mm test tubes in a test tube rack, a glass stirring rod, and a timer.

II. Determining the Effect of Reactant Concentrations on the Reaction Rate

NOTE: Complete determinations 1, 2, and 3, using the volumes of reactants and distilled water listed in Table 2.

Determination 1

7. Dispense, from the buret, 5.00 mL of $H_2C_2O_4$ solution into a clean, dry 20 × 150-mm test tube.

8. Dispense, from the buret, 6.00 mL of distilled water into the $H_2C_2O_4$ solution in the test tube.

   Thoroughly mix the contents of the test tube by stirring with a glass stirring rod.

⚠ CAUTION

**Potassium permanganate solution will discolor skin and stain clothing.
Use gloves when handling this solution. Prevent eye, skin, and clothing contact.
In case of a spill, immediately notify your laboratory instructor.**

NOTE: To determine the initial reaction time, start the timer when you have added half of the $H_2C_2O_4$ solution to the $KMnO_4$ solution.

9. Dispense, from a buret, 1.00 mL of the $KMnO_4$ solution into a second test tube.

NOTE: As the reaction in Step 10 proceeds, the solution color will change from purple to red to yellow. Stop the timer when the last trace of red disappears and the solution is yellow.

10. Quickly transfer the $H_2C_2O_4$ solution from its test tube into the test tube containing the $KMnO_4$ solution.

   Start the timer when you have added half of the $H_2C_2O_4$ solution to the $KMnO_4$ solution.

Thoroughly mix the contents of the test tube by stirring with a glass stirring rod. Place the test tube in the test tube support.

Stop the timer when the last trace of red disappears and the solution is yellow. Record in Table I on Data Sheet 1 the volume and molarity of each reactant, the volume of distilled water, and the elapsed time.

11. Repeat Steps 7–10 until you can reproduce the elapsed time to within 10 s. Record your data in Table II of Data Sheet 1.

Determinations 2 and 3

12. Follow the same procedure as used in determination 1 (Steps 7–11), using the quantities of reagents designated for determinations 2 and 3 in Table 2. Record all elapsed times in Table I on Data Sheet 1.

13. Transfer the reaction mixtures into the container labeled "Discarded Reaction Mixtures" provided by your laboratory instructor.

III. Determining the Effect of Temperature on the Reaction Rate

Determination 4

14. Fill a 600-mL beaker half full of warm tap water. Heat the beaker on a hot plate until the water temperature is 10–12 °C above room temperature. Stir the heating water to distribute the heat. Keep the water temperature constant to ±1 °C by adding ice or increasing the heat while you perform Steps 16–21.

NOTE: In Table III of Data Sheet 2, record the temperature of the water in the bath when the timer was started and the elapsed time of the reaction when the last trace of red disappears from the reaction mixture.

---

15. Dispense 5.00 mL of $H_2C_2O_4$ solution into a clean, dry 20 × 150-mm test tube.

16. Dispense 6.00 mL of distilled water into the test tube containing the $H_2C_2O_4$ solution.

Thoroughly mix the contents of the test tube by stirring with a glass stirring rod.

Support the test tube in the warm-water bath.

17. Dispense 1.00 mL of $KMnO_4$ solution into a second clean, dry 20 × 150-mm test tube.

Support the test tube in the warm-water bath.

18. After the solutions have warmed for about 10 min, rapidly transfer the $H_2C_2O_4$ solution into the test tube containing $KMnO_4$ solution.

Start the timer when you have transferred half of the $H_2C_2O_4$ solution.

Suspend the test tube containing the reaction mixture in the warm-water bath. Thoroughly stir with a glass stirring rod.

19. Stop the timer when the last trace of red disappears from the reaction mixture, leaving a yellow solution. Record the elapsed time on Table III of Data Sheet 2.

20. Repeat Steps 15–19 until you can reproduce the elapsed time to within 10 s. Record all warm-water bath temperatures and elapsed times in Table III on Data Sheet 2.

Determinations 5 and 6

21. Adjust the hot plate temperature to heat the water bath to a temperature 20 °C above room temperature. Stir the bath and keep the temperature constant, as you did in Step 14, while you perform Step 22.

22. Follow the same procedure as you used in Steps 15–20, using the quantities of reagents designated for determination 1 in Table 2. Record all elapsed times in Table III on Data Sheet 2.

23. Adjust the hot plate temperature to heat the water bath to a temperature 30 °C above room temperature. Stir the bath and keep the temperature constant, as you did in Step 21, while you perform Step 24.

24. Follow the same procedure as you used in Steps 15–20, using the quantities of reagents designated for determination 1 in Table 2. Record all elapsed times in Table III on Data Sheet 2.

25. Transfer all reaction mixtures to the "Discarded Reaction Mixtures" container.

    Drain the solution remaining in the $H_2C_2O_4$ buret into the "Discarded $H_2C_2O_4$ Solution" beaker.

    Drain the solution from the $KMnO_4$ buret into the container provided by your laboratory instructor and labeled "Discarded $KMnO_4$ Solution".

26. Transfer the solution from your "Discarded $H_2C_2O_4$ Solution" beaker into the container designated by your laboratory instructor and labeled "Discarded $H_2C_2O_4$ Solution". Wash the test tubes with soap or detergent if necessary. Rinse the burets and test tubes with tap water. Invert the burets, with stopcocks open, and place in the buret clamps to drain.

CAUTION

Wash your hands thoroughly with soap or detergent before leaving the laboratory.

CALCULATIONS

(Do the following calculations and record the results on your Data Sheets.)

II. Determining the Effect of Reactant Concentrations on the Reaction Rate

Do the following calculations for determinations 1, 2, and 3, and record the results in Table II of Data Sheet 1.

1. Calculate the initial $KMnO_4$ concentration in the reaction mixtures for each determination, using Equation 16.

initial $KMnO_4$ concentration, mol/L =

$$\left(\frac{\text{volume of } KMnO_4 \text{ solution added, mL}}{\text{total volume of reaction mixture, mL}}\right)\left(\begin{array}{c}\text{concentration of } KMnO_4\\\text{solution added, mol/L}\end{array}\right)$$

(Eq. 16)

2. Calculate the initial $H_2C_2O_4$ concentration in the reaction mixtures, using Equation 17.

initial $H_2C_2O_4$ concentration, mol/L =

$$\left(\frac{\text{volume of } H_2C_2O_4 \text{ solution added, mL}}{\text{total volume of reaction mixture, mL}}\right)\left(\begin{array}{c}\text{concentration of } H_2C_2O_4\\\text{solution added, mol/L}\end{array}\right)$$

(Eq. 17)

3. Calculate the average elapsed time, in seconds, for each determination.
4. Calculate the reaction rate for each determination, using Equation 15.
5. Calculate the reaction order with respect to $H_2C_2O_4$, x in Equation 14, using the method of initial rates.
6. Calculate the reaction order with respect to $KMnO_4$, y in Equation 14, using the method of initial rates.
7. Calculate the overall reaction order.
8. Calculate the rate constant, k, for the reaction. Use data from any single determination and Equation 12 to make the calculation.
9. Write a rate equation for the reaction of $KMnO_4$ solution with $H_2C_2O_4$ solution under the reaction conditions used in determinations 1–3.

III. Determining the Effect of Temperature on the Reaction Rate

Do the following calculations for determinations 4, 5, and 6, and record the data in Table III of Data Sheet 2.

10. Calculate the average temperature for each determination.
11. Calculate the average elapsed time for each determination.
12. Calculate the reaction rate for each determination.
13. Compute the average factor by which the elapsed time is decreased with each 10-degree increase in temperature. Divide the elapsed time for determination 4 by the elapsed time for determination 5. Divide the elapsed time for determination 5 by the elapsed time for determination 6. Average these two results.
14. Compute the average factor by which the reaction rate is increased with each 10-degree increase in temperature. Divide the reaction rate for determination 4 by the reaction rate for determination 5. Divide the reaction rate for determination 5 by the reaction rate for determination 6. Average these two results.

_____   _____   _____

Post-Laboratory Questions

(Use the spaces provided for the answers and additional paper if necessary.)

1. When you calculated k in the rate equation for the reaction of $KMnO_4$ solution and $H_2C_2O_4$ solution, you assumed k had the same value under the conditions of determinations 1, 2, and 3.

    (a) What assumption did you make about the reaction of $KMnO_4$ solution and $H_2C_2O_4$ solution in those determinations that allowed you to consider k to be a constant?

    (b) Would it be sound practice to compare the results of determinations 4–6 when calculating k? Briefly explain.

2. Do your experimental data substantiate the rule of thumb regarding the effect on the reaction rate of a 10-degree increase in reaction temperature? Briefly explain.

3. Consider the reaction that occurs when a ClO_2 solution and a solution containing hydroxide ions (OH^-) are mixed at 0 °C, shown in Equation 18.

$$2ClO_2(aq) + 2\ OH^-(aq) \rightarrow ClO_3^-(aq) + ClO_2^-(aq) + H_2O(l) \qquad \text{(Eq. 18)}$$

When solutions containing ClO_2 and OH^- in various concentrations were mixed at 0 °C, the following rate data were obtained:

Determination number	Initial concentration of ClO_2, mol/L	Initial concentration of OH^-, mol/L	Initial rate for formation of ClO_3^- mol/L · s
1	1.25×10^{-2}	1.30×10^{-3}	2.33×10^{-4}
2	2.50×10^{-2}	1.30×10^{-3}	9.34×10^{-4}
3	2.50×10^{-2}	2.60×10^{-3}	1.87×10^{-3}

(a) Use the method of initial rates to find the order of the reaction with respect to ClO_2 and with respect to OH^-. Write the rate equation for the reaction of ClO_2 and OH^- at 0 °C.

(b) Calculate the rate constant, k, for the reaction of ClO_2 and OH^- at 0 °C.

(c) Calculate the reaction rate for the reaction ClO_2 and OH^- at 0 °C when the initial ClO_2 and OH^- concentrations are 8.25×10^{-3} mol/L and 5.35×10^{-2} mol/L, respectively.

name section date

Data Sheet 1

I. Preparing to Measure Solution Volumes

concentration of $H_2C_2O_4$ solution, mol/L _____
concentration of $KMnO_4$ solution, mol/L _____
room temperature, °C _____

II. Determining the Effect of Reactant Concentrations on the Reaction Rate

Table I

Determination number	Volume of $H_2C_2O_4$ solution, mL	Volume of $KMnO_4$ solution, mL	Volume of water, mL	Elapsed time, s
1				
	average elapsed time, s			
2				
	average elapsed time, s			
3				
	average elapsed time, s			

Table II

Determination number	Calculated initial concentrations, mol/L		Average elapsed time, s	Reaction rate, mol/L · s
	$H_2C_2O_4$	$KMnO_4$		
1				
2				
3				

Order of reaction with respect to:

(a) $H_2C_2O_4$ _____

Overall reaction order _____

(b) $KMnO_4$ _____

Calculated rate constant, k, for the reaction _____

     Rate equation for the reaction:

_____   _____   _____
name   *section*   *date*

Data Sheet 2

III. Determining the Effect of Temperature on the Reaction Rate

Table III

Determination number	Volume of $H_2C_2O_4$ solution, mL	Volume of $KMnO_4$ solution, mL	Volume of water, mL	Temperature, °C	Elapsed time, s
4					
		average temperature, °C			
		average elapsed time, s			
5					
		average temperature, °C			
		average elapsed time, s			
6					
		average temperature, °C			
		average elapsed time, s			

On average, the reaction time is decreased _____ times when the reaction temperature was raised 10 °C.

On average, the reaction rate is increased _____ times when the reaction temperature was raised 10 °C.

---

name   section   date

Pre-Laboratory Assignment

1. Briefly identify the hazards you must be aware of before you work with:

(a) $H_2C_2O_4$ solutions

(b) $KMnO_4$ solutions

2. Briefly explain the meaning of the following terms as they pertain to this experiment.

(a) reaction rate

(b) rate equation

(c) rate constant

(d) overall reaction order

3. The method of initial rates involves substituting the initial reactant concentrations into rate calculations. When you do the experiment, you will be given $KMnO_4$ and $H_2C_2O_4$ solutions of known concentrations. Will you use these known concentrations in your rate calculations? Briefly explain.

4. Consider the reaction of ammonium ions (NH_4^+) and nitrite ions (NO_2^-), shown in Equation 19.

$$NH_4^+(aq) + NO_2^-(aq) \rightarrow N_2(g) + 2H_2O(l) \qquad \text{(Eq. 19)}$$

Solutions containing NH_4^+ and NO_2^- were mixed in various quantities and the following rate data at a constant temperature were obtained:

Determination number	Initial NH_4^+ concentration, mol/L	Initial NO_2^- concentration, mol/L	Initial rate for formation of N_2, mol/L · s
1	0.150	7.50×10^{-3}	3.04×10^{-7}
2	0.150	1.50×10^{-2}	6.08×10^{-7}
3	0.300	1.50×10^{-2}	1.22×10^{-6}

(a) Use the method of initial rates to find the order of the reaction with respect to NH_4^+.

(b) Use the method of initial rates to find the order of the reaction with respect to NO_2^-.

(c) Calculate the rate constant, k, for the reaction of NH_4^+ and NO_2^-.

(d) Write the rate equation for the reaction of NH_4^+ and NO_2^-.

Laboratory Techniques: Qualitative Inorganic Analysis Techniques

Prepared by Norman E. Griswold, Nebraska Wesleyan University

INTRODUCTION

Some people seem to think that a chemist is capable of analyzing practically any substance or mixture merely by looking at a sample or by performing a few simple tests. However, those who study chemistry know that analysis is not that easy. At present, there are 106 known elements that combine in many ways to form an immense number of compounds, each with its own characteristic set of properties. As a result, a combination of very sophisticated techniques is often required to analyze most samples.

Nonetheless, the method of **qualitative inorganic analysis** provides a simple procedure for separating and identifying approximately one-fourth of the known metallic elements from mixtures of inorganic compounds, without the need for elaborate procedures or expensive instruments. In addition, some qualitative inorganic analysis schemes include procedures for the analysis of a number of commonly encountered anions.

The most common method for separating components in the usual qualitative inorganic analysis scheme is **selective precipitation**, although some ions can be separated by conversion to gases or by formation of complexes. Selective precipitation can be used to separate approximately 30 metal ions and nearly a dozen anions. This method involves standard laboratory equipment such as beakers, burners, casseroles, crucibles, flasks, and test tubes. After separation, the individual ions can be identified using colors, odors, crystalline appearance, and solubility characteristics.

Several other techniques are used regularly in qualitative inorganic analysis and also, with some adjustments, in other laboratory work. Frequently these specific operations are described only in general terms, for example: "heat the solution in a test tube," "evaporate the solution to dryness," "mix the reagents until a precipitate forms," and "separate the precipitate and wash it thoroughly." Such general directions lead you to ask the following practical questions: How can a solution be heated in a test tube without the solution boiling out of the test tube? How can I do an evaporation without spattering the sample or burning it? How can reagents be mixed most effectively? How can I separate precipitates from the solutions in which they form? How do I wash a precipitate?

The answers to these and other practical questions concerning the techniques used in qualitative inorganic analysis are given in the sections that follow. Study these directions before beginning your laboratory work, and keep them handy for quick review when your analysis procedure specifies a particular technique. Sometimes an experienced laboratory instructor may suggest alternative ways to perform some of the operations described; there is more than one acceptable way to carry out some of these operations.

An important general point is to avoid carelessness in your laboratory work. Experience has shown that reasonably careful laboratory technique is required if the qualitative inorganic analysis scheme is to be a success.

SOME PRELIMINARY SUGGESTIONS

Preparing for the Laboratory

It is very important to prepare for laboratory work before actually going into the laboratory. Such procedures as heating solutions and allowing precipitates to form and settle can require considerable time. You should plan to do other work during these waiting periods. Study all of the procedures you expect to use. If the procedure lists an unfamiliar technique, reread the appropriate section in this module. Make the necessary preparations in your laboratory notebook for recording observations and other data. All this should be done *before* you enter the laboratory. Laboratory work periods are scheduled for performing analyses and generally do not allow time for study or preparation.

Keeping Your Laboratory Notebook

The necessity of keeping a complete, up-to-date, honest record of laboratory work in a laboratory note-book cannot be overemphasized. Inorganic analysis involves too many ions and too many tests for you to rely upon your memory as your source of information. For example, in many analysis schemes, metal ions that form insoluble sulfides in acid solution are separated into one group for analysis. The complete analysis of this group of eight ions may require as many as 25 tests. The result may be four black precipitates, three yellow precipitates, a red precipitate, an orange precipitate, and a colorless solution, if all eight ions are present in the sample. Frequently, however, some ions are not present in the sample. This complicates the situation, because some of the nine precipitates will not be found. When the analysis is completed and a report is being prepared, questions such as the following might be raised: Was the yellow precipitate lead(II) chromate, or was it cadmium sulfide? Was the black precipitate the result of a test for bismuth, for mercury, or for tin? Was the colorless solution a positive test for tin or a negative test for cadmium? These questions are difficult to answer without accurate laboratory notes.

A further problem is that some analyses cannot be completed in one laboratory period. As much as a week may pass before an analysis is resumed. A week is too long a period over which to remember the identities of solutions and/or precipitates in eight or ten test tubes. Such problems can be resolved quite simply. Record *all* of your observations in your notebook, and label *all* of your samples and containers.

Use a bound notebook, rather than loose pages or paper, for entering your observations and comments. A bound notebook is much less likely to be lost, and the binding keeps the pages in the proper sequence.

Many experimental results can be recorded in tabular form, so you should consider using tables where possible, such as for summaries of the results of your analyses.

Develop the habit of recording observations promptly. Describe your observations and comments in sufficient detail, so that you can reconstruct each step of the analysis later. Write down what you *actually* see or smell rather than what you *expect* to observe. If one of your analytical tests does not work properly, record the results and label them "faulty." Such an entry may be important at a later stage of the analysis. If you need help from your laboratory instructor at some point, a well-kept notebook will be helpful in determining the sequence of tests that you performed and in reviewing your conclusions resulting from your observations.

Label all containers that hold solutions or precipitates. The best devices for labeling are either glassmarking pencils or small squares of paper and rubber bands. Gummed labels can be used, but they can dry out and peel off the container. If you use a letter or numerical system, you should use the same labeling system with the corresponding entries in your notebook.

Your laboratory instructor will tell you exactly how to make entries in your notebook.

Avoiding Sample Contamination and Cleaning Equipment

Neat, careful, orderly laboratory work is essential in qualitative inorganic analysis to avoid sample contamination. Samples can become contaminated in subtle ways. For example, tap water contains such ions as Ca^{2+}, Mg^{2+}, Fe^{3+}, HCO_3^-, and Cl^-, so a container rinsed with tap water may contain unwanted ions. For this reason, only distilled or deionized water should be used in the analysis. All equipment should be cleaned regularly and rinsed with distilled or deionized water for further use. In the remainder of this module, the term "distilled water" refers to either distilled or deionized water.

Allow some time at the end of each work period for cleaning all equipment. Dirty equipment is much easier to clean immediately after use. Quickly scour the equipment with a test tube brush dipped in warm water containing dishwashing detergent. Rinse the equipment a few times with tap water to eliminate the suds, and then rinse several times with small amounts of distilled water. Tap water is used for the detergent solution and the first rinses because the distilled water supply is generally limited. Wipe dry the outside surfaces of equipment. Store the equipment in an inverted position to allow the inside surfaces to drain dry. Contamination can be introduced into flasks and beakers if their inside surfaces are wiped dry. By following this procedure, your equipment will be clean, dry, and ready for use during the next work period.

The laboratory bench top is also a notorious source of unwanted contaminants. Therefore, your working area must be kept clean. Equipment that will contact the sample, such as stirring rods, capillary pipets, and droppers, should be placed on a clean towel or sheet of paper at the edge of your working area. This practice reduces the likelihood of contamination and makes such equipment readily available when needed.

Using Chemicals and Discarding Chemical Waste

Many chemicals are toxic and/or corrosive. Be especially careful of ammonia, thioacetamide, and concentrated acids, but consider all chemicals as potentially harmful. Immediately wash off any chemical that contacts your skin using plenty of water, whether or not you feel a burning sensation. Wear safety goggles at all times to avoid harming your eyes with spattered chemicals.

Carefully read all container labels. Solutions can be made in a large range of concentrations. Sometimes more than one concentration of the same solution is used in a single experiment. Use of the wrong concentration could lead to unexpected results. Some solids can exist as strips, wire, granules, or powder, and sometimes the use of the correct form of solid is extremely important. Also, some substances have names that appear to be the same but are not identical. Compare, for example, sodium nitrate and sodium nitrite, tin(IV) chloride and tin(II) chloride, or hydrochloric acid and perchloric acid. Be absolutely certain that you are using the correct substance and the correct concentration.

While you are performing the analyses, you will have to discard some solid items such as matches, indicator paper, and filter paper. If your workspace is not near a waste container for paper, use a beaker labeled "waste paper" as a personal waste jar. This practice will save a lot of trips back and forth to the end of the laboratory bench or across the room. The beaker should be emptied at the end of each work period into a container designated by your laboratory instructor.

Occasionally, you will break glassware. You must clean up the broken glass immediately and discard it following the directions of your laboratory instructor.

Federal law now requires that all chemical waste be handled according to established regulations. This law requires segregating waste according to hazard categories and dealing with each category in the prescribed fashion. Some waste can be poured directly into the drain, but much of it cannot. Discarded mercury compounds qualify as hazardous waste materials, although discarded silver compounds can be processed and recycled. Be sure to follow the directions of your laboratory instructor for discarding solutions and residues from each experiment.

At the end of each laboratory session, it is important to wash your hands thoroughly with detergent or soap. This action will reduce the risk of skin irritation from chemicals or ingestion of traces of chemicals remaining on your hands.

PREPARING SUPPLEMENTARY EQUIPMENT

For qualitative analysis, a fairly standard set of laboratory equipment is assigned, consisting of such items as beakers, flasks, and test tubes. However, there are three kinds of items that are sometimes not made available as part of the regular equipment. These are a wash bottle, stirring rods, and capillary pipets.

Preparing and Using a Wash Bottle

A wash bottle is not absolutely necessary, but it is very useful for rinsing equipment and transferring precipitates. The wash bottle also contains a supply of distilled water and saves numerous trips to the distilled water tap. Some typical wash bottles are shown in Figure 1. A polyethylene squeeze bottle with a delivery tube makes a good wash bottle and is currently used in many laboratories. However, this type of wash bottle cannot be heated.

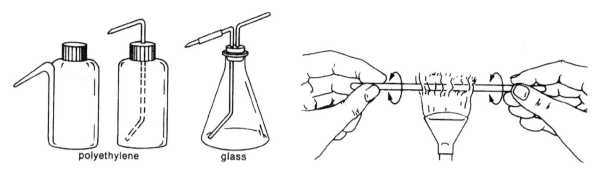

Figure 1
Some typical wash bottles

polyethylene   glass

Figure 2
Bending glass tubing

If one of these bottles is not available, you can construct a wash bottle by using a flask, a two-hole stopper, and two pieces of glass tubing. A handy flask size is 125 or 250 mL, and 6-mm glass tubing is commonly used. The longer piece of tubing should be at least 10 cm longer than the height of the flask. Insert this piece into a two-hole rubber stopper, positioning the tubing so that one end almost touches the bottom of the flask when the stopper is inserted tightly in the flask. The correct procedure for inserting glass tubing into a rubber stopper is given in **TECH 324, Laboratory Techniques: Safety Precautions**, in this series.

Sharply bend a second piece of tubing so that the bend is positioned above the stopper, as shown for the glass wash bottle in Figure 1.

To bend glass tubing properly, uniformly heat the tubing in the flame of a Bunsen burner fitted with a wing top, until the tubing is soft over a length of about 6 cm. Continuously rotate the tubing in the hottest part of the flame, as shown in Figure 2.

The flame will become yellow around the heated tubing, and the tubing will begin to sag a little. When you can no longer hold the tubing straight, remove the tubing from the flame, bend it to the desired angle, and allow it to cool. Make the slight bend on the end of the tubing that will be inside the bottle, using the same technique. Because you will often use the wash bottle in a slightly tipped position, the slight bend is needed to keep the bottom of the tubing beneath the surface of the distilled water when there is only a small volume of distilled water in the flask. Fire polish both ends of this tubing. Attach a fire-polished dropper tip to the end of the tubing outside of the flask, using a short length of rubber tubing.

The second, much shorter, piece of tubing extends about 10 cm above the stopper and should be bent using the same technique. Fire polish both ends of this tubing. When the tubing is cool, carefully insert it into the stopper (see Figure 1). Because any bend is generally the weakest place in a piece of tubing, you should resist the inclination to insert the tube by grasping the bend.

Preparing and Using Stirring Rods

If glass stirring rods are not supplied, make several from glass rods of 4- to 6-mm diameter. Cut the rod into suitable lengths. About 12 cm is suitable for 75-mm test tubes, but shorter lengths work better in small beakers. The proper cutting technique is as follows: Place the rod flat on the laboratory bench top. Using one firm stroke, make a scratch at the desired place on the rod with a triangular file or a glass-tubing scorer. Grasp the rod with both hands, one on either side of the scratch, which should be on the side away

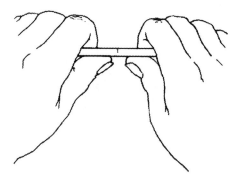

Figure 3
Hand position for breaking glass rod

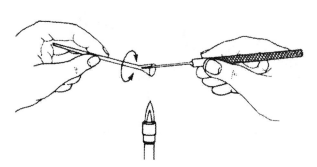

Figure 4
Flaring glass tubing with a heated file

from your body. Place your thumbs on the side opposite the scratch, as shown in Figure 3. Break the rod by simultaneously bringing your elbows in against the sides of your body and quickly pushing forward on the rod with your thumbs. The rod should break easily. Fire polish both ends of each stirring rod.

The main uses for stirring rods are: stirring solutions to ensure thorough mixing of reagents, testing the acidity of solutions with indicator paper, and dislodging precipitates.

Preparing and Using Capillary Pipets

Medicine droppers of about 1-mL capacity are usually available with the standard set of equipment assigned for qualitative inorganic analysis. These droppers usually deliver about 20 drops per mL. However, capillary pipets are often more convenient for withdrawing and transferring solutions from test tubes and centrifuge tubes. Basically, a capillary pipet is like a medicine dropper, except that a capillary pipet has a longer and narrower tip and delivers as many as 40 drops per mL.

Disposable Pasteur pipets may be available for these purposes. If not, you can make capillary pipets from 7- or 8-mm glass tubing. Cut the tubing into 15- to 20-cm lengths, using the technique for cutting glass rod described in the previous section. Remove the wing top from the Bunsen burner. Light the mixture of gas escaping from the burner, and adjust the flame to give a well-defined inner cone. Hold the piece of tubing with the center just above the bright blue cone of the flame, and rotate the tubing continuously, using both hands. When the hot portion of the tubing is very soft, remove the tubing from the flame, and slowly pull the two ends in opposite directions until the middle of the tubing is the desired thickness. Hold the tubing still until the glass hardens again. Cool the tubing on a ceramic-centered wire gauze for about 10 min. Make a scratch with a triangular file or a glass-tubing scorer at the point where the glass is thinnest, and separate the tubing halves. Carefully fire polish the constricted tips, making sure you do not seal them shut.

Next you will place a rubber dropper bulb on the large end of your capillary pipet. Frequently, the large end of the pipet must be flared so that the dropper bulb will fit snugly. To flare the pipet end, hold the wider end of the pipet in the burner flame just above the blue cone. Continuously rotate the pipet. At the same time, heat the narrow, pointed end of a triangular file in the flame. When the flame about the pipet becomes bright yellow, remove the pipet and insert the heated end of the file into the tubing at an angle. Rotate the pipet until the end is flared sufficiently, as shown in Figure 4.

If a glass ridge is desired on the flared end, reheat the end of the pipet with constant rotation. When the end is soft, hold the pipet vertically and press the end against a metal surface. After the pipet has cooled, attach a rubber bulb to the tubing. The capillary pipet will then be ready for use.

Calibrate each of your pipets by counting the number of drops while using it to deliver several milliliters of distilled water into a 10-mL graduated cylinder.

When using the pipet, always hold it at the same angle you did while calibrating it. Your pipets should deliver 30 to 40 drops per mL. Label each pipet with the number of drops per mL. A capillary pipet is very useful for adding small amounts of reagent, but note the precaution about adding volumes by pipet in the section on measuring reagents.

MAKING OBSERVATIONS

In most cases, conclusions about the presence or absence of ions in a solution are based on formation of precipitates, color changes, flame tests, or evolution of gases.

Precipitate Formation

A solid that forms in a solution when solutions of reagents are mixed is called a **precipitate**. Formation of a precipitate makes a solution appear cloudy. Precipitates may range from coarse particles to gelatinous or fluffy solids to a suspension of particles so fine that individual particles cannot be seen. Milk is a suspension. The formation or disappearance of precipitates gives important information about whether or not certain ions are present in a solution.

Color Changes

A **solution** is a clear mixture of one or more solutes in a solvent such as distilled water. The word "clear" means that no precipitate is present to make the solution appear cloudy. The term "clear" does not indicate anything about the color of the solution. A solution without cloudiness is clear, but a solution without color is colorless. Sodium chloride dissolved in water is a clear, colorless solution, but copper(II) sulfate dissolved in water is a clear, blue solution. A solution cannot be cloudy and colorless.

If a solution changes color when reagents are mixed, a reaction has occurred. A change of color must be interpreted carefully. For example, formation of a cloudy, green solution may indicate any one of the following possibilities:

(1) a green precipitate in a colorless liquid,

(2) a white precipitate in a green liquid,

(3) a green precipitate in a green liquid,

(4) a blue precipitate in a yellow liquid, or

(5) a yellow precipitate in a blue liquid.

Consequently, you should separate the solids from the liquids before making decisions about the meanings of color changes. The liquid remaining after a precipitate has been removed is called the **supernatant liquid**. Supernatant liquids are clear but may be colored. Techniques for separating the precipitate from the supernatant liquid are discussed later in this module.

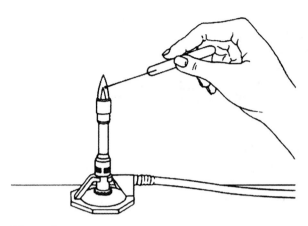

Figure 5
The flame test

Figure 6
Detecting odors

Flame Tests

The presence of certain cations can be confirmed by **flame tests**. A flame test is performed by dipping a special wire into a solution of the cation and then holding the wire in a Bunsen burner flame. Sodium ions give a bright yellow flame, barium ions a green flame, and potassium ions a purple flame. Other cations also have characteristic flame colors.

The wire should be a piece of platinum or nichrome sealed in the end of a piece of glass tubing. A small loop is formed at the end of the wire, and the tubing is used for holding the wire. The wire is first cleaned by dipping it in 6M HCl and then heating it in a Bunsen burner flame as shown in Figure 5. Note that the wire is not placed in the hottest part of the flame but at the edge. Repeat the cleaning procedure until no color appears when the wire is placed in the flame. Then dip the wire in the test solution, heat the wire in the flame as before, and note any color. For comparison, always repeat this test with a solution known to contain the suspected cation.

Evolution of Gases

The presence of certain anions is indicated by the evolution of a gas. These reactions occur frequently when an acid is added to a solid. Many gases are colorless, but their presence can be detected by their odor or the appearance of bubbles. To detect the odor, wait until vigorous bubbling has subsided, hold the test tube near your nose, but not pointed at your face, and waft vapors toward your nose as shown in Figure 6. ***Do not place the test tube directly under your nose and inhale.***

A few gases, such as NO_2, are colored. To see these clearly, hold the test tube against a white background, and note any color in the space above the solution.

MEASURING REAGENTS

Liquids

Qualitative inorganic analysis procedures require the addition of liquid reagents in either drop or milliliter amounts. Actual drops vary in size, but the drops referred to in the procedures of the experiments in this series are assumed to have a volume of 0.05 mL. Many standard medicine droppers deliver drops of approximately this volume; thus there are about 20 such drops per mL. The droppers should be calibrated to make sure that they deliver approximately 20 drops per mL. However, note that capillary pipets deliver much smaller drops. When a procedure specifies the addition of a certain number of drops, use a medicine dropper rather than a capillary pipet. All additions of liquids in amounts of up to two or three milliliters should be made with droppers rather than with a graduated cylinder. The addition of larger amounts of solutions is seldom called for, but graduated cylinders are sufficiently accurate for measuring volumes larger than 3 mL.

Solids

Amounts of solid substances can be measured by using a triple-beam balance, a centigram balance, or a top-loading balance that is sensitive to at least 0.05 g. The correct procedure for using these balances is given in **TECH 329, Laboratory Techniques: Mass Measurement**, in this series.

Weighing by difference is the best procedure to use when measuring solids. This procedure consists of determining the mass of the solid and its container, pouring out the solid until the required amount has been removed, and then weighing the container and remaining solid. Chemicals should always be placed on the balance in an appropriate container. Never put chemicals directly on the balance pan.

Sometimes the exact amount of solid to be added is not important. This is indicated by directions such as, "Add some solid..." or "Add approximately...." In such cases, you can estimate the amount of solid you are adding. Such estimates are simplified if you know the approximate mass of a heaping spatula-full of some common solids, such as ammonium nitrate or ammonium sulfate. For example, if you know that a spatula can hold about 0.15 g of a common inorganic salt, then the direction to add approximately 0.3 g of ammonium sulfate can be followed by adding two heaping spatula-fulls of the salt.

Estimations using spatulas and droppers can save considerable time, provided that a supply of clean droppers and a clean spatula are readily available.

TRANSFERRING REAGENTS

Because of the nature of qualitative inorganic analysis, it is of utmost importance to avoid contaminating either the sample or the reagents used. The following techniques are designed to maintain the purity of all chemicals.

Liquids

Take an appropriate container to the reagent shelf where the liquid is kept. Make the actual transfer at a nearby sink to avoid spills on the laboratory bench, shelf, or floor. If the general supply bottle is equipped with a dropper, use the dropper, but be sure that it never touches the container or its contents, as shown in Figure 7 on the next page.

If the general supply bottle is equipped with a stopper, the stopper should either be held during the transfer or placed on its flat top. Do not lay the stopper on its side on the laboratory bench or shelf. The proper technique is shown in Figure 8 on the next page. Do not put your dropper or capillary pipet into the general supply bottle. Pour chemicals from the general supply bottle into a labeled container for personal use. Be sure the appropriate stopper is returned to the supply bottle. Use a clean dropper to dispense liquids from your labeled container.

Solids

Take an appropriate container to the reagent shelf where the general supply chemicals are kept. Solids are somewhat more difficult to transfer than are

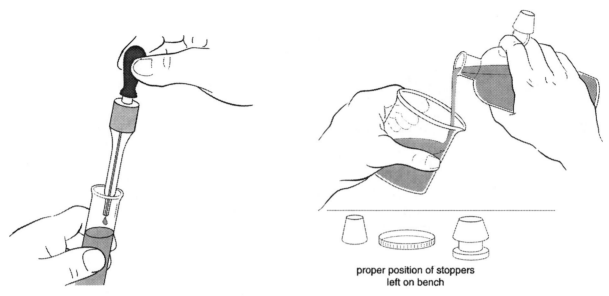

Figure 7
Transferring a liquid using a dropper

Figure 8
Pouring a liquid

liquids, so a wide-mouth container such as a beaker is preferable. Make the transfer at or near the reagent shelf.

During the transfer, do not contaminate the stopper. Hold it or lay it on the laboratory bench, as shown in Figure 8. You should never use your spatula in the general supply bottle. Solid chemicals are most easily poured by tipping the general supply bottle. Slowly rotate the bottle back and forth about an imaginary axis passing through the top and bottom of the bottle, as shown in Figure 9. Mere tipping of the bottle alone often causes large pieces

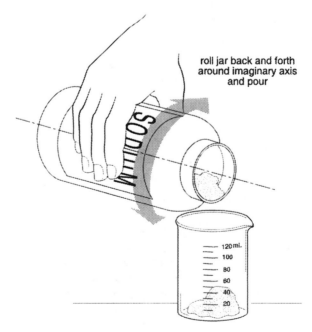

Figure 9
Pouring a solid

of solid to fall out of the bottle, leading to spills. Be sure the right stopper is returned to the general supply bottle. Do not interchange stoppers between bottles.

MIXING REAGENTS

Students often underestimate the importance of thoroughly mixing reagents. Reactions cannot occur unless reagents are mixed. Mixing of reagents is a difficult operation because most reactions are carried out in narrow test tubes. You should not try to mix chemicals by holding a cork or your thumb over the top of the test tube while shaking it. This may cause contamination of the sample. Instead, the following mixing techniques are best.

A stirring rod rinsed with distilled water can be used for mixing. Both vertical and rotary movement of the rod should be used for the most satisfactory results. If the test tube is almost full, be sure that its contents will not overflow when the stirring rod is inserted.

For a test tube that is less than half full, use the following mixing method. Grasp the top of the test tube with the thumb and forefinger of one hand, and sharply tap or snap the test tube several times near the bottom with your other forefinger. It may seem an unlikely technique, but it produces no splashing and works quite efficiently.

For centrifuge tubes which are tapered at the bottom, or for test tubes that are more than half full, efficient mixing can be accomplished as follows. Draw up a portion of the solution into a clean capillary pipet. Then, squirt the solution back into the tube near the bottom. This procedure should be repeated at least two or three times. You may also pour the liquids back and forth from one test tube to another to achieve mixing, but you must take care to avoid spilling the solution during the transfer.

If you need to mix liquid chemicals with water, always add the concentrated chemical to water, rather than vice versa. This procedure keeps the new solution dilute at all times and avoids many accidents. Usually additions should be made slowly, using small amounts of the reagent being added. It is especially important to add acid to water because of the heat generated by the dilution.

If you need to dissolve a solid in a liquid, add the solid to the liquid, rather than vice versa. Solids should be added in small amounts with stirring, except under special circumstances.

DETERMINING THE ACIDITY OF A SOLUTION

An operation that must be performed quite often in qualitative inorganic analysis is the determination of whether a solution is acidic or basic. For this purpose, a variety of kinds of indicator paper are available in narrow strips less than 1 cm wide. These indicator papers are saturated with either a single indicator, as with litmus paper, or with a mixture of indicators, as with indicator papers that have several colors over a wide range of pH values.

Litmus paper is used when you want to know whether a solution is either acidic or basic, without needing to know the specific pH. Litmus paper is red in acidic solutions and blue in basic solutions. If, however, the procedure requires a solution with a specific pH (within a narrow range), then you should use special indicator papers. The choice of paper depends upon the application. If, for example, you need a solution with the acidity of a 0.3M HCl solution (pH 0.5), then you should use methyl violet paper, because it is yellow-green at this acidity. There are also mixed indicator papers that change colors over narrow pH ranges.

Do not dip the indicator paper directly into the solution in a test tube for the following reasons: (1) The strips are generally too short to reach the solution in the test tube, (2) the sample may become contaminated by dissolved indicator and paper fibers, (3) such a procedure would test mainly the acidity of the droplets at the top of the test tube, rather than the acidity of the entire solution, and (4) the use of a whole strip for only one test is inefficient.

An acceptable method for testing the acidity of a solution with indicator paper is: (1) Dip a clean, dry glass stirring rod into the thoroughly mixed solution, (2) stir vigorously, (3) withdraw the rod carefully to avoid touching the inside walls of the test tube, and (4) touch the end of the rod to one spot on the indicator paper. In this way, a 4- or 5-cm strip of indicator paper can be used for several tests, and there is less risk of solution contamination.

HEATING SOLUTIONS

Liquids in test tubes are best heated by holding the tube with a test tube clamp and placing the test tube in a 250-mL beaker of boiling water. A 250-mL beaker is small enough to permit the test tubes to remain upright during heating. Many tests require the heating of solutions, so get in the habit of heating water in a beaker at the beginning of each work period. Keep the water hot throughout the work period. Do not let the water level in the beaker get too low. Keep the beaker one-fourth to two-thirds full. If tap water leaves a scale on the beaker as the water evaporates, you can remove the scale at the end of the work period by adding water to the beaker, cooling the water for a short time, and carefully adding a small amount of dilute hydrochloric acid to the water.

Larger amounts of liquids in beakers and flasks are best heated by placing the container on a ceramic-centered wire gauze on a ring stand, supporting the container with a clamp. Heating liquids for evaporation is described in the next section.

EVAPORATING A SOLUTION

Qualitative inorganic analysis procedures frequently require reducing the solution volume or evaporating a solution to dryness. These techniques need considerable attention and caution must be taken to avoid sample loss by spattering, generation of toxic or unpleasant fumes, or decomposition caused by overheating. However, if proper methods are used, evaporation can be accomplished without sample loss. When acids or other solutions that emit toxic or unpleasant fumes must be evaporated, the procedure must be performed under a fume hood.

The most convenient container to use for evaporation is a porcelain casserole. However, the casserole handle is short and quickly becomes hot while the casserole is being heated. The handle can be extended and kept cooler by slipping a two-inch length of heavy-wall rubber tubing over about half of the handle. Do not push the rubber tubing too close to the casserole bowl, or the rubber may get hot and melt or burn. In some cases, crucibles and beakers can be used for evaporation, as described below.

As a heat source for evaporation, a microburner is best, if it is available. The microburner should be adjusted so that the flame is about 12 mm. If a microburner is not available, a Bunsen burner can be substituted, as long as it is adjusted to produce a small flame. If necessary, use a screw clamp on the burner tubing to make this adjustment. Small amounts of liquid can be evaporated by placing the liquid in a casserole under an infrared lamp, but this method is rather slow.

When evaporating a solution in a casserole, constantly swirl the casserole while heating. Avoid getting the liquid too hot, or it will boil vigorously and spatter out of the casserole. If the solution is being evaporated to dryness, remember that the casserole retains quite a bit of heat. Thus, you should stop heating the casserole before evaporation is complete. The heat retained by the casserole will then complete the process. It is a good idea to have withdrawn a little of the liquid being evaporated in a dropper or capillary pipet before beginning the evaporation. Then, if the casserole seems to be overheating, you may add one or two drops of the liquid, to prevent baking of the residue. However, it is better to stop the heating early enough to avoid the need for addition of the extra liquid.

If the solution is in a small beaker, and the liquid needs only to be partially evaporated, you can hold the beaker with crucible tongs over a burner flame and swirl the beaker and its contents gently in the flame. It is crucial to hold the beaker properly, with both jaws of the tongs outside the beaker. To grip only one side of the beaker with one of the jaws of the tongs inside the beaker is a sure way to contaminate the sample. The proper way to hold a container with crucible tongs is shown in Figure 10. The beaker should be less than half full at the beginning of the heating, and the evaporation should not be carried to dryness when using a beaker. Crucibles can also be used for evaporation by following this method.

A crucible can be used for evaporation in an air bath, which can be constructed from a beaker and a wire triangle, as shown in Figure 11.

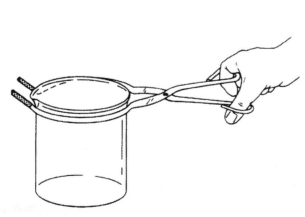

Figure 10
Holding a beaker with crucible tongs

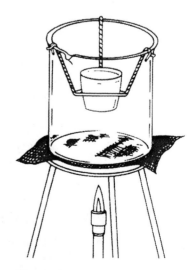

Figure 11
Evaporating a solution using an air bath

This method gives uniform, but slow, evaporation, although care must be taken to avoid getting the beaker too hot and breaking it.

FORMING A PRECIPITATE

Most of the tests in qualitative inorganic analysis involve the formation of precipitates and their complete separation from the remaining supernatant liquid. These operations are necessary to ensure that a given ion is precipitated completely, so that the ion does not interfere with later tests. The precipitate needs to be completely free of the solution, for the same reason. This section and the four that follow describe the methods that will best assure success in this aspect of inorganic analysis.

When you anticipate the formation of a precipitate, slowly add the precipitating agent, using a dropper or capillary pipet. Mix the solutions constantly, using one of the methods described in the section on mixing reagents. Formation of large particles is favored if you warm the solution in a hot water bath.

Always check for completeness of precipitation. After heating the mixture, let the precipitate settle in the test tube, or centrifuge if necessary. Add another one or two drops of precipitating agent. If more precipitate forms, add additional amounts of precipitating agent and reheat the solution. Check again for completeness of precipitation. Avoid adding too much precipitating agent; a large excess can sometimes dissolve the precipitate by forming a complex ion.

A few comments must be made about the precipitating agent, thioacetamide. This substance is used as a precipitating agent for more than half of the metal ions in the usual qualitative analysis scheme. It reacts with water to supply sulfide ion for precipitation of metal sulfides. The reaction in water is

$$\underset{\text{thioacetamide}}{CH_3-\overset{\overset{\textstyle S}{\|}}{C}-NH_2(aq)} + 2\,H_2O(l) \xrightarrow{\text{heat}} CH_3-\overset{\overset{\textstyle O}{\|}}{C}-O^-(aq) + NH_4^+(aq) + H_2S(g)$$

Although thioacetamide is safe to use when handled prudently, you should be aware of its less desirable properties. First, thioacetamide has exhibited carcinogenic properties in some animal feeding studies. Consequently, it is prudent to avoid skin contact with a thioacetamide solution and to wash your hands thoroughly with soap or detergent after using this solution. Second, both thioacetamide and the product H_2S are toxic, so it is prudent to use small amounts and to work under a fume hood, if possible. Finally, H_2S has a foul odor that is described as a "rotten-egg smell," and this odor is minimized if small amounts of thioacetamide are used under a fume hood.

USING THE CENTRIFUGE TO SEPARATE PRECIPITATES

Once a precipitate has formed, it must usually be separated from the remaining solution. Although this can be done by filtration, it is often faster and just as effective to use a centrifuge. A **centrifuge** is a device that holds test tubes or other similar containers and spins them in order to separate the components into two distinct phases. The mixture of solid and liquid is rotated at high speed, which exerts as much as 300 to 400 times the force of gravity on the precipitate. The force causes the precipitate to settle quickly and pack at the bottom on a test tube. The remaining supernatant liquid can be separated from the precipitate by decanting or by using a capillary pipet. The precipitate is then usually washed thoroughly to remove traces of supernatant liquid. The great advantage of using the centrifuge is the short time required for a precipitate to settle to the bottom of the test tube. In most cases, the centrifuge does not have to be run at top speed for more than about 1 min, although some light, fluffy precipitates may require several minutes for separation. The following precautions should be observed when using the centrifuge.

Mixtures are ordinarily centrifuged in test tubes. However, because of the terrific force exerted on the test tubes, you should examine them carefully to make sure that they are free of any flaws before using them in the centrifuge. If there is only a tiny amount of precipitate in the test tube, you may prefer to use a centrifuge tube that is tapered at the bottom.

The head of the centrifuge revolves at speeds in excess of 1000 rpm, so your hands and clothes must be kept clear of the spinning parts. The centrifuge must be carefully balanced at all times. Two test tubes should always be inserted into the centrifuge, one containing the solution being centrifuged and the other containing an equal volume of water. The tubes should be placed directly opposite each other in the centrifuge head. Centrifuge heads usually have four or more compartments for test tubes. When you are sharing the centrifuge with someone else, be sure that the tubes are properly labeled so that they can be identified after the centrifuge stops spinning.

Occasionally a test tube will shatter in a centrifuge because of the intense force placed on it. If this happens, do not immediately peer into the centrifuge to check the damage. The likelihood in such a case of being cut by flying glass particles is high if you open the centrifuge before it has completely stopped. Nothing can be done until the centrifuge has stopped.

Many centrifuges must be allowed to coast to a stop after the motor has been turned off. Some centrifuges have mechanical brakes or can be stopped by hand pressure. Be extremely careful if you use your hand to slow the centrifuge head. The head should be slowed gradually to avoid mixing the precipitate into the solution again, injuring your hand, or damaging the centrifuge.

REMOVING SUPERNATANT LIQUID FROM A PRECIPITATE

In some cases involving precipitates such as silver chloride or lead(II) sulfate, centrifugation packs the precipitate so tightly in the bottom of the test tube that the supernatant liquid can be separated from the precipitate by pouring off the liquid into another test tube. This procedure is called **decanting**. However, precipitates such as sulfides or hydroxides are usually packed less firmly. In such cases, a capillary pipet is required for removal of the supernatant liquid. The bulb is squeezed before the pipet is inserted into the supernatant liquid, and the liquid is removed in small portions.

If a precipitate does not centrifuge completely or appears to be stirred up when you are using a pipet to remove the supernatant liquid, you may isolate the precipitate as follows. Twist a small piece of cotton wadding, and insert it into the tip of a clean dropper. Do not stuff the wadding down into the barrel of the dropper. Leave a tuft of the wadding protruding from the dropper. Draw the supernatant liquid through the cotton, which will trap any loose precipitate. Remove the wadding and release the clear supernatant liquid into a clean test tube. Repeat as necessary. This procedure filters precipitate particles from the supernatant liquid.

The supernatant liquid should always be retained unless you are *absolutely positive* you will have no further use for it. Additional dissolved ions are often contained in the liquid, and the liquid is sometimes used for later tests. Be very sure that this is not the case before you discard this liquid.

WASHING A PRECIPITATE

After the supernatant liquid has been removed from the precipitate, there will still be an appreciable amount of solution clinging to the wet precipitate. Because the remaining solution may contain ions that could interfere with later tests, the last traces must be removed by washing the precipitate. Washing is also necessary for retaining soluble ions in the supernatant liquid that are to be tested for later. If a fraction of the soluble ions is lost with each precipitation, there may be insufficient ions in solution for the later tests to be successful.

The wash liquid is usually distilled water, although dilute hydrochloric acid and other solutions are sometimes used. Experience has shown that several washings with small portions of wash liquid are more effective than one washing with a large amount. The procedure for washing follows.

Add a small amount of wash liquid to the packed precipitate. Use a stirring rod to break up the precipitate. Thoroughly mix the precipitate and the wash liquid. Centrifuge again and decant or withdraw the wash liquid as before. The first wash liquid is often added to the supernatant liquid from the first centrifugation, because the wash liquid may contain an appreciable amount of soluble ions to be tested for later. Repeat this washing procedure at least two or three times. These later washings are often discarded.

TRANSFERRING A PRECIPITATE

If possible, plan your laboratory work so that you can avoid transferring precipitates from one container to another. This procedure is not very efficient. However, sometimes precipitation is carried out in such a large volume of solution that the mixture must be centrifuged in more than one test tube. In this case, after centrifugation, the precipitates should be recombined before continuing the analysis. To do this, transfer the precipitate as follows.

Add distilled water to the precipitate you wish to transfer. If necessary, use a stirring rod to break up the packed precipitate and form a suspension, but be certain to use distilled water to rinse off any precipitate clinging to the rod, before removing the rod from the test tube. Then, transfer the precipitate by drawing small portions of the suspension into a dropper and quickly depositing them into the other container. Carefully clean the dropper after you have transferred all of the precipitate.

SUMMARY

If you use the techniques discussed in this module, you will significantly increase the chances that you will complete your qualitative inorganic analyses efficiently and successfully. One final observation: Generally, analysis procedures are quite detailed and often tell exactly how much reagent to add and what to do for each test. However, there are some variations in solution concentrations and other conditions from one laboratory to the next. Thus, there is no substitute for an alert, thinking mind that questions the reasons for each step in the procedure, is capable of interpreting observations, and can make appropriate adjustments when confronted now and then with an unfamiliar situation.

_____ _____ _____

Pre-Laboratory Assignment

1. Name two sources of sample contamination.

2. List five general rules for handling chemicals.

3. What is the most important general rule to follow when discarding chemicals and solutions?

4. What is the best procedure for weighing solids?

5. List four precautions regarding the use of general supply bottles of chemicals.

6. What is the correct procedure for mixing an acid solution with water?

7. List four reasons for not dipping litmus paper or pH paper into solutions.

8. What should you do at the beginning of each laboratory session?

9. What test should be performed after each precipitation?

10. List six precautions to be followed when using the centrifuge.

11. Name two procedures used to separate precipitates from supernatant liquid.

12. Why must precipitates be washed after the supernatant liquid has been removed?

Making and Using Visible Absorption Measurements

*Prepared by Norman E. Griswold, Nebraska Wesleyan University, and
M. L. Gillette, Indiana University Kokomo*

PURPOSE OF THE EXPERIMENT

Use a spectrophotometer to obtain the visible spectrum of an absorbing species. Determine the analytical wavelength. Collect absorbance data and construct a Beer's law plot. Use the plot to determine the concentration of the absorbing species in a solution containing an unknown concentration of the species.

BACKGROUND INFORMATION

Quality-control analysts often need to determine the concentrations of various ions in a mixture. To do so, the analyst must be able to distinguish each component in the mixture from all others. For example, quality-control analysts at a winery need to monitor the copper ion concentration in the company's wine. A common method is to pass electromagnetic radiation through the wine sample, and measure the amount of radiation transmitted or absorbed by either the sample's components or the compounds formed by the sample's components. We refer to this method as **spectroscopic analysis**, because we measure the amount of radiation transmitted or absorbed using a spectrophotometer. Each element has a characteristic absorption pattern. The unique absorbance characteristics of the individual components of a solution allow us to determine the concentration of one substance in the presence of others.

Electromagnetic radiation varies over an extremely wide range of wavelengths, from 1×10^3 to 1×10^{-10} cm. We classify spectroscopic analysis by the region of the electromagnetic radiation spectrum used for the analysis. Three especially useful regions are the **infrared (IR), visible (VIS),** and **ultraviolet (UV)**. The wavelength range encompassed by each of these regions is shown in Figure 1 on the next page.

We can also use electromagnetic radiation from these spectral regions for purposes other than identification. For instance, we can study the stretching and bending of covalent bonds from their response to IR radiation. We can use ultraviolet and visible spectroscopy to study the

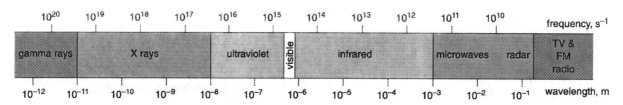

Figure 1
The electromagnetic spectrum, including the UV, VIS, and IR regions

energy levels of the outer electrons of radiation-absorbing species, as well as to distinguish among geometric isomers.

Another important use for visible spectroscopy is determining the concentration of a colored solute. As the method's name implies, the wavelengths of light used for visible spectroscopy are all visible to the human eye. Therefore, we can study only colored substances using visible spectroscopy. For example, a wine analyst could determine the copper ion concentration in a batch of wine by reducing the copper to copper(I) ion (Cu^+) and then adding cuproine (biquinoline), forming the intensely violet Cu^+–cuproine complex. After extracting the Cu^+–cuproine complex into 3-methyl-1-butanol (isoamyl alcohol), the analyst could then use visible spectroscopy to measure the concentration of the complex, and calculate the concentration of copper ion in the wine.

I. Spectrophotometers

A **spectrophotometer** is an instrument that measures the interaction between electromagnetic radiation and a sample. The instrument consists of a light source, a diffraction grating to separate the light into its component wavelengths, and lenses and slits to focus the light. A photoelectric device detects the amount of light passing through the sample and displays a measure of this amount on a meter or digital display. Several manufacturers produce spectrophotometers for visible spectroscopy. Among the most common are those in the Spectronic 20 series, made by Spectronic Instruments, which have digital or analog displays, depending on the model. Both versions are shown in generalized form in Figure 2.

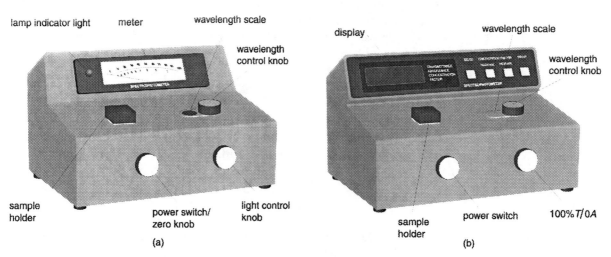

Figure 2
Spectronic 20-series instruments showing (a) analog and (b) digital displays

The **sample holder** has a hinged cover that opens to permit insertion of a sample cuvet and closes to keep out stray light. **Cuvets** are specially designed test tubes used to hold samples in the sample holder. Cuvets have specific dimensions, allowing reproducible results. They are made of a specific type of glass that does not absorb visible radiation.

Some manufacturers equip their spectrophotometers with fiber-optic probes, which eliminate the need for cuvets. Flow-through cells, with entrance and exit portals, are also available for some instruments. Using such cells, we can evaluate concentration changes as a function of time, data that are important in kinetics and extraction studies.

We turn on the spectrophotometer by rotating the **power switch/zero knob** clockwise until it clicks. We then use the same knob to adjust the display to indicate zero percent transmission (0%T) with the sample holder empty.

A schematic diagram of the Spectronic 20 optical system is shown in Figure 3. In the Spectronic 20, white light, containing all of the visible wavelengths, emanates from a tungsten lamp and passes through an entrance slit and two lenses to a diffraction grating. A **diffraction grating** is a sheet of plastic-coated glass engraved with many fine, accurately spaced, parallel grooves. The grating acts as a prism. White light hitting the grating is separated into visible wavelength components (colors) that are reflected in a fan-shaped pattern (a **spectrum**). The shortest visible wavelengths (violet) are at one end of the spectrum, and the longest visible wavelengths (red) are at the other.

We can rotate the grating with the **wavelength control knob**. By rotating the grating, we focus a specified narrow band of wavelengths of light on a second slit, which narrows the light bandwidth even further. Finally, our selected wavelength (which can be read on the display) strikes the sample. The light that passes through the sample hits a **phototube detector**, which measures the amount of transmitted light.

The display readout of a spectrophotometer varies, depending on the specific model. Some spectrophotometers, such as the Spectronic 20 and the Spectronic 21MV, display analog readings on meters, using two scales: a nonlinear **absorbance** (A) scale ranging from zero to infinity, and a linear **percent transmittance** (%T) scale ranging from zero to 100%. The linearity of the %T scale enables more accurate readings than those obtained using

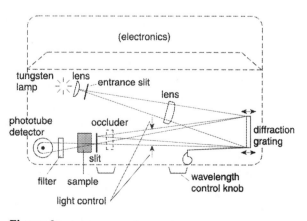

Figure 3
Schematic diagram of the Spectronic 20 optical system

the absorbance scale. Other spectrophotometers, such as the Spectronic 20D and the Spectronic 21D, feature a digital display that enables us to read percent transmittance and absorbance directly with equal accuracy.

Because absorbance data are often more useful than percent transmittance data for component analysis, usually we either read absorbance directly from a digital display, or we read percent transmittance and convert it to the equivalent absorbance. To understand this conversion process, we must first define percent transmittance in mathematical terms, as shown in Equation 1. In this equation, I_t is the intensity of the light transmitted by the sample, and I_o is the intensity of the light directed at the sample. A decrease in the intensity of the transmitted light, as compared with the intensity of the original light source, indicates that some of the light has been absorbed by the sample.

$$\%T = \left(\frac{I_t}{I_o}\right)(100) \tag{Eq. 1}$$

We then rearrange Equation 1 to form Equation 1a.

$$\frac{\%T}{100} = \frac{I_t}{I_o} \tag{Eq. 1a}$$

By taking the logarithm of Equation 1a, we obtain Equation 2.

$$\log\left(\frac{\%T}{100}\right) = \log\left(\frac{I_t}{I_o}\right) \tag{Eq. 2}$$

Mathematically, we define **absorbance** as shown in Equation 3.

$$A = \log\left(\frac{I_o}{I_t}\right) \tag{Eq. 3}$$

Therefore, $\log(I_t/I_o) = -A$. Using Equations 2 and 3, we can derive Equation 4:

$$-A = \log\left(\frac{\%T}{100}\right) \tag{Eq. 4}$$

We can use Equation 4 to convert experimental $\%T$ data to the equivalent absorbances, as follows:

Divide $\%T$ by 100.

Take the logarithm of this answer.

Change the sign of the answer.

Sometimes, more than one species in a solution absorbs radiation at the same wavelength. We compensate for this by preparing a **reference solution**, also called a **blank**. The reference solution contains all of the solution components *except the one whose concentration we wish to determine*. With a cuvet containing the reference solution in the sample holder, we use the **light control knob** to adjust the readout to 100%T. In this way, the instrument will not register absorbance by any solution components other than the one whose concentration we are trying to measure.

II. Selecting the Analytical Wavelength

Most species that absorb visible radiation do so at a variety of wavelengths. To determine the most useful wavelength for analyzing a particular absorbing species, we must determine the visible **absorption spectrum** of the species. An absorption spectrum is a graph of the absorbance of a species versus wavelength.

Figure 4(a) shows a simple absorption spectrum, with one peak. Figure 4(b) shows the additive nature of the absorption spectra of substances A and B in the same solution. The solid curve is the absorption spectrum of the mixture. The dashed curves are the absorption spectra for the individual substances at the concentrations present in the mixture.

We use the optimum wavelength for a particular species, called the **analytical wavelength (λ_{max})**, for determining the concentration of that species. When selecting λ_{max}, we should consider the following:

A slight misadjustment in the wavelength setting should not produce an appreciable change in absorbance. For example, in the spectrum in Figure 4(a) the wavelength at Q is a better analytical wavelength than the wavelength at P, because the graph is at maximum absorbance at Q and not at P.

As we will discuss in the next section, the absorbance of a solution is proportional to the concentration of the absorbing species. We want to select an analytical wavelength at which significant species concentration changes produce significant absorbance changes. In Figure 4(a) if we reduced the solution concentration by 50%, the absorbance would be at points R and S for the two wavelengths shown. Because the difference in absorbance between Q and R is greater than the difference in absorbance between P and S, the analytical wavelength corresponding to points Q and R is preferable to that for P and S. Thus, the best analytical wavelength for the substance whose spectrum is shown in Figure 4(a) is the wavelength corresponding to the maximum absorbance.

In solutions containing more than one absorbing substance, we try to select an analytical wavelength at which only the substance whose concentration we are trying to determine has significant absorption. For example, in Figure 4(b), the wavelength at X is preferable to the wavelength at Y for determining the concentration of substance A. Substance B absorbs very

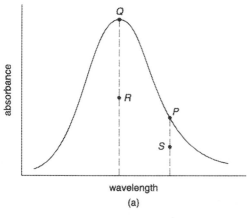

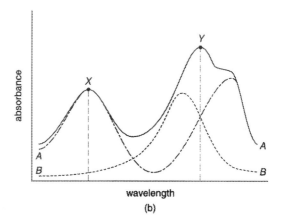

Figure 4
Two absorption spectra

little radiation at the wavelength at *X*, so it will not significantly affect the measurement of the concentration of substance *A*.

III. The Beer-Lambert Law

The amount of light absorbed by a solution is primarily influenced by three factors: the distance the light travels through the solution, *b*, usually measured in centimeters; the molar concentration of the absorbing solute, *c*; and the sensitivity of the solute to the light at the analytical wavelength. We refer to the sensitivity variable, which varies with wavelength, as the **molar absorptivity** (ε) of the solute. The mathematical relationship among these variables, known as the **Beer-Lambert law** or **Beer's law**, is shown in Equation 5.

$$A = \varepsilon bc \qquad\qquad (\text{Eq. 5})$$

Because the internal diameters of most cuvets used for absorption determinations are uniform, *b* is essentially constant. When we perform analyses using a fixed analytical wavelength and cuvets of uniform size, both ε and *b* are constant. The absorbance of a solution becomes directly proportional to the molar concentration of the absorbing species. In such cases, a graph of *A* versus *c*, called a **Beer's law plot**, should be a straight line, as shown in Figure 5.

To generate data for a Beer's law plot, we prepare a series of **standard solutions**, containing known concentrations of the colored species we are analyzing. We determine the absorbance of each standard solution at the analytical wavelength. Then we use these data to prepare a graph of *A* versus *c*. If the plot is linear throughout the entire range of data points, we say that the system obeys Beer's law.

We can determine the concentration of the absorbing species in a solution of unknown concentration by measuring the unknown solution's absorbance at the analytical wavelength. Then we determine the corresponding concentration from our Beer's law plot for the substance. For example, in Figure 5, point *X* has an absorbance value of 0.420. The concentration that corresponds to $A = 0.420$ is indicated by point *Y* and has the value $20 \times 10^{-5} M$.

Sometimes the absorbance of an unknown solution turns out to be greater than the absorbance of the most concentrated standard solution measured for the Beer's law plot. Because of the uncertainties associated

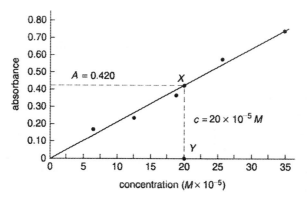

Figure 5
A Beer's law calibration plot

with extrapolating the plot, we systematically dilute the concentrated unknown solution until its absorbance falls within the range of absorbances shown on our Beer's law plot. Then, we take the dilution factor into consideration when we calculate the concentration of the original unknown solution.

Deviations from the Beer-Lambert law can occur due to either of the following factors:

- High solution concentration If a solution is sufficiently concentrated that the solute particles interact with each other, then the effective concentration will differ from the calculated concentration.

- Interaction between the absorbing species and the solvent

In this experiment, you will analyze the absorptivity of the assigned substance in solution. To do so, you will determine the absorption of a series of standard solutions of the substance, after determining the analytical wavelength for the substance. From your data you will construct a Beer's law plot. Using the plot, you will determine the concentration of the substance in a solution containing an unknown concentration of the substance.

PROCEDURE

Preview

Prepare notebook or data sheet for data collection

Prepare standard solutions

Set up spectrophotometer and prepare cuvets

Obtain absorbance–concentration data for a Beer's law plot

Obtain absorbance data for a solution containing an unknown amount of the solute

Determine concentration of the solute in unknown solution

CAUTION

Wear departmentally approved eye protection while doing this experiment.

NOTE: During the Procedure, you may want to refer to Figure 2 in order to review the locations of various parts of the Spectronic 20 (assuming that you are using this model).

---

1. Preparing Your Laboratory Notebook or Data Sheet for Collecting Data

In your laboratory notebook, record the identity of your assigned absorbing substance and its analytical wavelength. If the analytical wavelength is not supplied, you must determine it in Step 4 from the visible spectrum of the absorbing substance. Leave sufficient space for recording a range of percent transmittances and equivalent absorbances. Record these data at intervals of 10–20 nm throughout the visible spectrum, as shown in the table in Post-Laboratory Question 1(a).

For your Beer's law plot data, prepare a data table that includes spaces for the molar concentration of each standard solution, its %T, and its calculated A, as shown in the table in Post-Laboratory Question 2(a). If the spectrophotometer you are using has a digital display, your laboratory instructor may prefer that you record absorbance directly.

Prepare a similar data table for the solutions of unknown concentration you will be studying, including space for the identification code of each solution.

If you are using a prepared data sheet, check to be certain that it includes spaces for each of the entries described above.

2. Preparing Standard Solutions

Prepare four or five standard solutions of your assigned substance to generate a Beer's law plot. Include at least one solution that is more concentrated than you anticipate any of your unknown solutions will be. Your laboratory instructor will tell you what the maximum concentration range of the unknown solution is and will give you specific directions for preparing your standard solutions. Record the concentrations of your standard solutions in your data table.

3. Turning on the Power to the Spectrophotometer

Turn the power switch/zero knob clockwise until it clicks. The lamp indicator light should light. Your laboratory instructor will tell you whether or not your instrument must warm up before use.

4. Zeroing the Spectrophotometer

Make certain that the sample holder is empty and the cover is closed. Adjust the zero knob until the display reads 0%T.

5. Using a Cuvet Containing a Reference Solution (Blank)

If you are studying solutions consisting of a single absorbing substance dissolved in distilled or deionized water, use distilled or deionized water as your reference solution, or blank. If you are studying solutions containing several components, use a reference solution composed of all solution components except the colored species whose concentration you wish to determine.

Handle a cuvet by its upper rim only. Finger oil or smudges on the lower part of the tube will affect the light passing through that part of the tube.

Rinse a cuvet with three small portions of the appropriate reference solution (blank). Dispose of the rinses as directed by your laboratory instructor.

Half fill your cuvet with the reference solution. Wipe the outside of the cuvet with a lint-free tissue or lens paper to remove any fingerprints or smudges.

6. Setting the Light Control Knob

If the cuvet has a vertical line etched on it, orient the cuvet so that the line faces the front of the spectrophotometer. Firmly put the half-filled cuvet in the sample holder. Close the sample holder cover. Adjust the light control until the display reads 100%T.

Remove the cuvet from the sample holder. Retain this cuvet and its contents. Use it periodically to re-check the settings for 0% and 100%T.

7. Selecting the Wavelength

Adjust the wavelength control knob to the analytical wavelength for your assigned species. If you have not been given this wavelength, select it from the visible spectrum of the absorbing substance. To determine the visible spectrum, half fill a clean cuvet with your assigned species, wipe the outside surface of the cuvet with a tissue, and place the cuvet in the sample holder. Record wavelength and %T readings as you change the wavelength knob 10–20 nm. Convert the %T readings to A, using Equation 4, and plot the data. From the resulting spectrum, choose an analytical wavelength and record the analytical wavelength in your laboratory notebook or on your data sheet.

8. Obtaining Data for a Beer's Law Plot

Using the reference solution (blank), check 0%*T* and 100%*T* settings.

Rinse a clean cuvet three times with small portions of your *least* concentrated standard solution. Discard the rinses as directed by your laboratory instructor. Half fill the cuvet with the least concentrated standard solution. Wipe the cuvet with a tissue. Firmly seat the cuvet in the sample holder, and close the cover. Read the %*T* indicated on the meter, or read the absorbance if your instrument has a digital readout. Record the %*T* or absorbance in your laboratory notebook or on your data sheet. Remove the cuvet from the sample holder. Discard the solution as directed by your laboratory instructor.

Rinse the cuvet three times with the next more concentrated standard solution, discarding the rinses as directed. Half fill the cuvet with this standard solution. Read and record the %*T* or absorbance of this solution.

Repeat this procedure for each of your remaining standard solutions, in order of increasing concentration. Check the 0%*T* and 100%*T* settings with your reference solution after each determination. Record all data in your laboratory notebook or on your data sheet.

When you are finished, remove the cuvet and rinse it three times with distilled water. Discard the rinses as directed by your laboratory instructor.

9. Obtaining Absorbance Data for Solutions with Unknown Concentrations

Rinse the cuvet three times with small portions of your unknown solution. Discard the rinses as directed. Half fill the cuvet with your unknown solution. Determine and record the %*T* or absorbance of this solution. Record this %*T* or absorbance in your laboratory notebook or on your data sheet.

If you wish to determine the absorbance of other unknown solutions of the same substance, recheck the 0%*T* and 100%*T* settings with your reference solution, and repeat Step 9. When you are finished, remove the cuvet and discard the solutions as directed.

10. Turning Off the Spectrophotometer

When you have completed all of your determinations, turn off the instrument *if no one else is waiting to use it*. To do so, turn the power switch/zero knob counter-cockwise until it clicks. The lamp indicator light should no longer be lit.

11. Cleaning the Cuvets

Rinse both the cuvets several times with tap water, then with distilled water. Pour rinses into the drain. Allow the cuvets to drain, or dry them in an oven at 110 °C. Store the dry cuvets in marked containers, in order to avoid confusing them with regular test tubes.

12. Processing the Data

If applicable, use a calculator or spreadsheet program and Equation 4 to convert all %*T* readings to equivalent absorbances. Record these absorbances in your laboratory notebook or on your data sheet.

13. Preparing a Beer's Law Plot

Your laboratory instructor may ask you to prepare your Beer's law plot using a graphing program. If so, you will be given instructions for using the program to prepare the graph. Otherwise, use the following procedure.

(a) Use a straightedge and sharp pencil to draw the axes. Label the vertical axis "absorbance" and the horizontal axis "concentration" or "molarity."

(b) Select an appropriate scale for each axis. The scale units on the two axes do not have to be the same size. Choose scale units that are large enough to allow easy interpolation.

(c) Plot the absorbance–concentration data for your standard solutions. Draw the best straight line through the data points. This line should also pass through the origin.

(d) Title your graph, using the name of the absorbing species and the analytical wavelength.

14. Interpreting the Absorbance Data for the Unknown Solution

Locate the absorbance of your unknown solution on the vertical axis of your Beer's law plot. Use a straightedge to find the point on the graph corresponding to this absorbance and mark it, as shown for point X in Figure 5. Now use your straightedge to determine the concentration that corresponds to this absorbance. Make a mark where the straightedge crosses the horizontal axis, as shown by point Y in Figure 5. Read and record the unknown solution concentration at this mark.

Repeat this procedure for any other unknown solutions whose absorption you determined.

CAUTION

Wash your hands thoroughly with soap or detergent before leaving the laboratory.

Post-Laboratory Questions

(Use the spaces provided for the answers and additional paper if necessary.)

1. A chemist determined the copper ion concentration in a batch of wine by formation and extraction of the Cu^+–cuproine complex into 3-methyl-1-butanol, obtaining the data shown below. There is 1 mol Cu^+ ion in 1 mol of Cu^+–cuproine complex.

   (a) Convert the %T data to equivalent absorbance data and record below. Plot the A versus (wavelength) data to prepare the visible absorption spectrum for the Cu^+–cuproine complex in 3-methyl-1-butanol.

λ, nm	%T	A	λ, nm	%T	A
360	2.51	_____	500	26.3	_____
380	31.6	_____	520	22.9	_____
400	55.0	_____	540	14.5	_____
420	66.1	_____	550	14.1	_____
440	69.2	_____	560	15.1	_____
460	63.1	_____	580	39.8	_____
480	36.3	_____	600	55.0	_____

   (b) Based on your spectrum, suggest the optimum analytical wavelength for the Cu^+–cuproine complex.

   (c) Would distilled water be an appropriate reference solution (blank) for this analysis? Briefly explain.

2. (a) The same chemist prepared five standard Cu^+–cuproine/3-methy-1-butanol solutions and measured their $\%T$ against a 3-methyl-1-butanol blank, using the analytical wavelength chosen in Question 1. Prepare a Beer's law plot of the chemist's data, shown below.

Cu^+–cuproine concentration, M	$\%T$	A
1.93×10^{-4}	6.3	_____
1.61×10^{-4}	10.0	_____
9.66×10^{-5}	25.1	_____
6.44×10^{-5}	38.9	_____
3.22×10^{-5}	64.6	_____

(b) The Cu^+ ion in 100 mL of the wine analyzed in Question 1 was complexed with cuproine and extracted into 3-methyl-1-butanol. The $\%T$ of this solution was 47.3% at the analytical wavelength. Calculate the mass of Cu^+ ion, in grams, present in 100 mL of the wine.

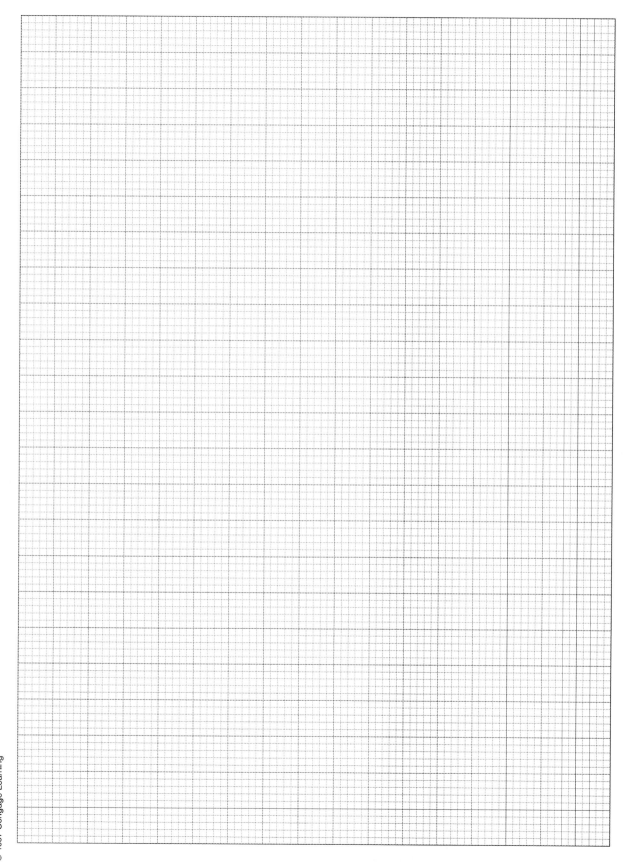

Name   Section   Date

Pre-Laboratory Assignment

1. Briefly define the following terms as they pertain to spectroscopic analysis.

    (a) reference solution or blank

    (b) absorption spectrum

    (c) analytical wavelength

    (d) standard solutions

    (e) Beer's law plot

2. Briefly explain why we perform the following procedures when doing spectroscopic analyses.

    (a) We perform the analysis using the analytical wavelength for the absorbing species.

    (b) We calibrate the $100\%T$ using a reference solution (blank), before we determine the absorbance of our samples.

    (c) We carefully wipe the outside of the cuvet before placing it in the sample holder.

(d) We dilute a solution of unknown concentration if the absorbance of this solution falls outside of the concentration range represented by our Beer's law plot.

3. A laboratory technician used spectroscopy to determine the titanium (Ti) content of a steel sample. The technician did so by extracting the Ti in the steel into a hydrogen peroxide (H_2O_2) solution. Titanium forms a yellow complex with H_2O_2. The analytical wavelength for the complex is $\lambda = 410$ nm. The technician obtained the following data, using a series of standard Ti–H_2O_2 solutions and the Ti–H_2O_2 solution extracted from the steel sample.

titanium concentration, M	%T	A
1.2×10^{-3}	13.8	_____
6.0×10^{-4}	36.1	_____
4.0×10^{-4}	51.3	_____
3.0×10^{-4}	61.1	_____
2.0×10^{-4}	70.8	_____
1.5×10^{-4}	80.0	_____
steel sample solution	18.4	_____

(a) Prepare a Beer's law plot for the Ti–H_2O_2 complex, using the grid on the next page.

(b) Determine the titanium concentration in the steel sample solution.